INSTANT LOSS COOKBOOK

The Definitive Weight Loss Cookbook for Health and Fitness

Joel Moyer

Table of Contents

PART I

Chapter 1: The Power of the Crock Pot and Its Benefits

The Ways You Can Benefit

Think of how many times you have experienced 'spells' that you did not feel like spending hours over the stove preparing dinner. Can you relate? How about the times during the holidays when you are planning on a houseful of guests; yikes? By the way, "Don't sweat it because you have your fabulous cooker and all of these new recipes to try out."

These are a few ways to make the path a bit easier:

Get Ahead of the Meal: Preparing food with your Crock-Pot® can put you ahead of the game the night before you have a busy day planned. You can always make the meal for the next day in just a few minutes. Put all of the ingredients (if they can combine overnight) into the pot, so when you get up the next morning; all you need to do is take it out of the fridge, and let it get to room temperature. Turn it on as you head out of the door and dinner will be ready when you get home. YES!

Save a lot of Effort and Time: All it takes is a few good recipes and a little bit of your valuable time. In most of the cases, these recipes are geared towards a fast lifestyle and will be ready with just a few simple steps. After some time and practice, you will know exactly which ones will be your favorites; all of them!

Cut Back on Dining Out: Having an enjoyable meal at home is so much more personal for your family because you (and your pot) prepared it!

Not only that, You will eliminate the temptation to order foods that might not be so healthy and in turn—will be more expensive.

Watching the Extra Liquids: There is no need to use additional ingredients, other than what is described within each of the recipes. Ideally, you should not fill the more than half to two-thirds full of ingredients. Too much liquid will cause a leakage from the top and may result in improperly cooked food.

Cook it Slow & Leave it Alone: A slow cooker is known for creating delicious dishes while bringing out all of the natural flavors. So, go ahead and go to work or have some fun—or—better yet go to bed early! There is no need to worry about checking on it (unless the recipe calls for it). Each time the lid is removed—valuable heat is escaping—resulting in a breakdown of the advised times. Just keep that element it in mind, even though it smells so good!

Trimming the Fat: One huge advantage to the use of this type of cooking is you can save quite a chunk of money purchasing cheaper cuts of meat. Also, capitalize on the flavorful meat in small quantities and by bulking up on veggies with smaller meat portions.

Hot Antioxidants

Many recent studies have discovered cooking some food items such as tomatoes will increase the bioavailability of many of the nutrients. For example, lycopene which is linked to cancer and heart prevention becomes move available to the body because the heat releases the lycopene.

A study from 2003 compared the content of fresh, frozen, and canned corn which was processed with heat; specifically lutein and xeaxanthin, and found less lutein in the fresh version. This lutein is mostly well-known to protect you from some eye diseases.

Score 'ONE' for the Crock-Pot®.

Who Knew?

Basic Times & Settings

The question always arises of how long you should cook your items if you don't have a recipe for a Crock-Pot®. These are only general guidelines because the size of a pot will make a difference in the cooking times.

Regular Cooking Times Hours	Crock Pot® High Temperatures	Crock Pot® Low Pot Temperatures
1/4 to 1/2	1 to 2	4 to 6
1/2 to 1	2 to 3	5 to 7
1 to 2	3 to 4	6 to 8
2 to 4	4 to 6	8 to 12

Note: You must consider that root veggies take longer than other vegetables and meats which mean they should be placed in the lower part of the pot.

Are You Ready? Of course, you are!

Chapter 2: Healthy Breakfast Recipes

Boiled Eggs

Did you ever wake up in the middle of the night for a 'potty' break, and decided you want some boiled eggs or egg salad for breakfast or work tomorrow, but do not have the time to sit around and wait for the eggs to cook? You have a cure for that!

Ingredients and Instructions

The simplicity is amazing!

1) Pour some water into the Crock-Pot®, add as many eggs as you want, and set the pot for 3 ½ hours on the low setting. Go back to bed and enjoy tomorrow!

One-Hour Bread

Crave that fresh bread—no longer! You can have some delicious comfort food shortly!

Ingredients

1 ½ C. Baking Mix

3 Tbsp. Italian Seasoning

½ cup milk (skim is okay)

Optional: ½ C. shredded cheese or 3 Tbsp. Grated Parmesan cheese

Directions

1) Prepare the cooker with some non-stick cooking spray.
2) Combine all of the ingredients until the lumps are gone and empty into the cooker.
3) *Notes:* Bisquick® is a good choice.

Breakfast Fiesta Delight

Directions

1 Pound Country-Style Sausage

1 Package (28-ounces) frozen hash brown potatoes (thawed)

½ Cup whole milk

12 large eggs

1 ½ Cups shredded Mexican blend cheese

Directions

1) Prepare the Crock-Pot® by spraying it with some cooking spray to help with the cleanup.
2) Brown and crumble the sausage in a frying pan; remove and pat the grease away using a paper towel.
3) Whip the eggs together in a mixing container.
4) Layer the ingredients with a layer of potatoes, cheese, sausage, and eggs.
5) *Serving Time*: Have some salsa, sour cream, pepper, and salt for a tasty topping.

Servings: Six to Eight

Prep Time is fifteen minutes

Cooking Time is six to eight hours.

Italian Sausage Scramble

Ingredients

1 ½ Lbs. Italian sausage

1 medium yellow onion

6 medium red potatoes

¼ Cup fresh Italian minced parsley

One medium diced tomato

1 Cup frozen/fresh kernel corn

2 cups grated Cheddar cheese

Directions

1) Discard the outer casing from the sausage. Peel and dice the onions and potatoes.
2) Sauté the onion and crumbled sausage until browned. Place them on a few paper towels to absorb the grease/fat and add the items to the slow cooker.
3) Combine the rest of the ingredients—blending well. Cover and cook.

Servings: Six

Prep Time is 15 Minutes.

Cook Time: The high setting is for four hours, and the lower setting is for six to eight hours.

The Sweeter Side of Breakfast

Blueberry Steel Cut Oats

Ingredients

1 ½ C. of water

2 C. frozen blueberries

1 banana

1 C. Steel cut oats

1- ½ C. Vanilla almond milk

1 Tbsp. butter

1 ½ tsp. cinnamon

Directions

1) Prepare a six-quart cooker with the butter, making sure to cover the sides also.

2) Mash the banana slightly and add all of the ingredients into the Pot—stirring gently.
3) Place the top on the crock pot and cook for *one hour* on the HIGH setting; switch to the WARM setting overnight, and sleep tight!

Wake up ready for a busy day by adding a drizzle of honey and get moving!

Servings: Four to Six

Preparation Time: Fifteen Minutes

Cooking Time: Eight hours

Pumpkin Pie Oatmeal

Ingredients

1 C. oats (steel cut)

3 ½ C. water

1 C. pumpkin puree

¼ tsp. each:

- salt
- vanilla extract
- pumpkin pie spices

Optional: 2 Tbsp. maple syrup

Directions

1) Use some non-stick cooking spray to coat the Crock-Pot®.
2) Empty the oats into the Pot.
3) Mix the remainder of the ingredients in a large mixing container, and pour over the oats.

4) *Note*: If you like sweeter oatmeal just adjust the flavor after it is cooked.

Cooking Time: Eight hours on low

Pumpkin Butter

Ingredients

4 Cups pumpkin

1 tsp. ground ginger

2 tsp. cinnamon

1-¼ Cups honey/maple syrup

½ tsp. nutmeg

1 tsp. vanilla extract (*optional*)

Instructions

1) Blend the vanilla, syrup/honey, and pumpkin puree in the Crock-Pot®.
2) Cover and cook. During the last hour—add the ginger, cinnamon, and nutmeg.
3) If you want it a little thicker, you can crack the lid. After all, the aroma is tantalizing—especially first thing in the morning!

You can store in jars in the bottom of the fridge for a healthy addition—anytime.

Yields: About 10 ounces

Preparation Time: Five Minutes

Cooking Time: Five hours

Chapter 3: Time-Saving Lunch Specialties

Beef Tacos

Ingredients

1 Package taco seasoning

1 (ten-ounce) Can tomatoes and green chilies (Rotel)

1 Pound lean ground beef

Directions

1) Add everything listed into your Crock-Pot®.
2) If you are available; stir every couple of hours to break up the beef or break it up before serving.
3) Serve on a floured tortilla or taco shell with your choice of toppings.

Servings: 12 tacos

Preparation Time: Two Minutes

Cooking Time: Five to Six Hours

Root Beer & BBQ Chicken

Ingredients

1 (18-ounce) bottle barbecue sauce

4 chicken breasts

¼ teaspoon each pepper and salt

½ can or bottle root beer (full-sugar)

Note: You can use Dr. Pepper or Coke instead of root beer.

Directions

1) Pour the drink of choice, and place the chicken in the cooker.

2) Drain once the chicken has finished cooking, and discard most of the liquid—but leaving enough to prevent dryness.
3) Flavor with some pepper and salt if desired and empty the contents of the sauce into the Crock-Pot®, cooking for about 15 to 20 minutes.
4) Enjoy on some burger buns or rolls.

Cooking Time: The high temperature will have it ready in 3 hours.

Stuffed Banana Peppers

Ingredients

1 Package Italian Sausage

Banana Peppers

2 Jars of Marinara Sauce (approximately)

Directions

1) Adapt this for your crowd on the amounts used.
2) Remove both ends of the peppers and scoop out the seeds and discard them.
3) Pour ½ of the jar of sauce in the Crock-Pot®.
4) Dice the sausage, in case it is not already prepared.
5) Stuff the pepper with the sausage and put them into the Pot.
6) Pour the sauce over the banana peppers.

Cooking Time: Low for eight to nine hours

Crock-Pot® Taco Soup

Ingredients

1 (14.5-ounces) Can Each:

- Beef broth
- Petite diced tomatoes

1 (15-ounces) Can Each:

- Black beans
- Corn

1 (10-ounces) Can Rotel Original

1 Can kidney beans (16-ounces)

1 (1-oz.) pouch each:

- Taco seasoning mix
- Ranch seasoning mix (Hidden Valley)

½ teaspoon salt

1 ½ teaspoons onion powder

1 Lb. ground beef

Garnish: Sour Cream, Fritos, chopped green onions, or some shredded cheddar cheese

Notes: The recipe is excellent if you choose the 'Diced Tomatoes with Green Chilies.'

Directions

1) Cook the beef and drain. Rinse and drain all of the cans of veggies except for the chilies; reserve the liquid from the corn and tomatoes.
2) Toss everything into the Crock-Pot® (except for the garnishes).
3) Cook for the necessary time.
4) When the process is completed, add the garnishes of your choice with some Fritos on the side to complement the flavors

Servings: 8 to 10

Prep Time: Ten minutes

Cook Time: Low for 4 hrs. or High for 2 hrs.

Chapter 4: Dinner in a Hurry

Beef

Meat for the Tacos

Ingredients

2 Lbs. Ground beef (lean)

1 cup diced onions/Birds Eye Chopped Onions and Garlic

1 Package low-sodium taco seasoning mix

Directions

1) Put the burger into the Crock-Pot® and cook it for four to six hours. If you are in the area of the kitchen—stir the meat every couple of hours to ensure it is cooking evenly (if not—no worries).
2) When the cooking cycle is complete; drain the beef on some paper towels.
3) Combine the onions and ½ to one package of the taco seasoning.
4) Blend well and continue cooking for about one more hour

Servings: Six

Preparation Time: Five Minutes

Cooking Time: Low setting: Four to Six hours

Steak Pizzaiola

Ingredients

1 (one to two pounds) London Broil

1 Yellow, orange, or red sliced bell pepper

1 Large sliced onion

¼ Cup water

½ to ¾ of a jar (your choice) tomato pasta sauce

Directions

1) Flavor the meat with the pepper and salt and place it into the Crock-Pot®.
2) Add the peppers and onions, followed by your favorite sauce,
3) Cook for six to eight hours. (Flip a time or two if you are home.)
4) Serve over some pasta, potatoes, or veggies.

Cooking Time: Low heat for six to eight hours

Steaks in the Pot

Ingredients

4 to 6 steaks

¼ C. White Wine

2 T. A-1 Sauce

2 T. Dijon mustard

Directions

1) Blend the mustard and steak sauce; add it to each of the pieces of steak.
2) Add the meat into the Crock-Pot®, add the wine, and cook for six to eight hours.

Servings: Four or More

Cooking Time: 6 to 8 Hours on the low setting

Chicken and Turkey

Buffalo Chicken

Ingredients

3 to 5 Pounds (no skin or bones) chicken breasts

1 (12-ounce) Bottle Red Hot Wings Buffalo Sauce

1 Pouch ranch dressing mix

Directions

1) Put the chicken into the Crock-Pot®. Empty the sauce over the breasts and sprinkle the ranch mix over the top. Cover and Cook.
2) Take the chicken out of the Pot and throw away the sauce.
3) Shred the chicken with a couple of forks. It should be tender.
4) Put it back into the cooker and stir to coat the chicken thoroughly.
5) Leave it in the pot on low about one more hour. Most of the sauce will be absorbed.

Cooking Time: Low for five hours

Caesar Chicken

Ingredients

1 bottle (12-ounces) Caesar dressing

4 skinless & boneless chicken breasts

½ Cup shredded Parmesan cheese

Directions

1) Add the breasts of chicken to the Crock-Pot®.
2) Cook the chicken for the specified time and drain the juices.
3) Empty the dressing over the breasts.

4) Sprinkle the cheese on top of that and cook for thirty more minutes covered until done.

Have a side of Caesar salad to complement the meal.

Servings: Four

Prep Time: 5 minutes

Cooking Time: Use the low setting for 6 hrs. ; the high setting High for 3 hrs.

Cranberry Chicken

Ingredients

4 (no skin or bones) Chicken Breasts

1 (8-ounces) bottle Kraft Catalina dressing

1 Pouch dry onion soup

1 (14-ounces) Can Ocean Spray Whole Cranberry Sauce

Directions

1) Cook the chicken in the Crock-Pot® according to your specified times. Drain the juices.
2) Combine the cranberry sauce, onion soup mix, and dressing. Empty it over the chicken.
3) Cook—covered—about 30 minutes.

Servings: Four

Preparation Time: Five minutes

Cooking Time: High for three hours or low for six hours

French Onion Chicken

Ingredients

4 Chicken breasts (no bones or skin)

1 Can French Onion soup (10.5-ounces)

½ cup sour cream

Directions

1) Put the breasts in the Pot and cook for the stated time. Empty the liquids.
2) Combine the soup and sour cream and add into the pot on top of the chicken

breasts.

3) Cook covered for about 30 minutes.

Servings: Four

Preparation Time: Five Minutes

Cooking Time: The high setting will take approximately three hours, whereas the low setting takes six hours.

Hawaiian Chicken

Ingredients

4 to 5 skinless and boneless breasts of chicken (thawed)

1 (20-oz.) Can Dole Pineapple Chunks

1 Bottle (12-oz.) Heinz Chili Sauce

1/3 C. brown sugar

Directions

1) Cook the chicken until its predetermined time limit is completed. Empty the liquid.
2) Combine the brown sugar, ½ of the juices of the can of pineapples, the chili sauce, and the chunks of pineapple.
3) Empty the mixture over the drained breasts and heat on the high setting for approximately 30 minutes or so.
4) Have a bit of pineapple in every bite. Yummy!

Servings: 4 to 5

Preparation Time: 5 min.

Cooking Time: High = 6 hrs. / Low = 3 hrs.

Honey Mustard Chicken

Ingredients

1 (12-ounces) Bottle Dijon mustard

1/3 C. honey

4 skinless & boneless chicken breasts (thawed)

Directions

1) Cook the chicken for its predetermined time and dispose of the juices.
2) Combine the mustard and honey in a small dish.
3) Empty the sauce over the chicken and cook for about ½ hour (covered) until done,

Servings: Four

Preparation Time: Five Minutes

Cooking Time: Use the low setting for six hrs. Or on high for three hrs.

Chicken Italian Style

Ingredients

4 chicken breasts (thawed – no bones- no skin)

1 (16-ounce) Bottle Italian Dressing

Directions

1) Place the breasts of chicken into your Crock-Pot® and pour the dressing on them.
2) Put the lid on and let it do your work!

Servings: Four

Preparation Time: 5 minutes

Cooking Time: Use the high setting to prepare the chicken for 3.5 hrs. Or use the low setting for 7 hours.

Swedish Meatballs

Ingredients

1 (12-ounce) jar Heinz HomeStyle Gravy (Savory Beef)

1 (eight-ounce) container of sour cream

1 Bag Frozen Meatballs

Instructions

1) Empty the gravy into the Crock-Pot®, followed by the sour cream.
2) Combine these until they are completely blended.
3) Toss the package of frozen meatballs into the Pot filling to approximately 2/3 to ¾ of the space.
4) Place the lid on the pot and cook—occasionally stirring if you happen to be close to the kitchen.
5) You can always make more or less of the recipe depending on how many people you will serve.

Cooking Time: Low for a minimum of 5 hours

Sweet and Sour Chicken

Ingredients

1 (22-ounces) Bag frozen Tyson Chicken Breast

2 Cups cooked rice/steamed vegetables (or both)

1 bottle (18-ounces) Apricot Preserves

1 jar (12-ounces) chili sauce

Directions

1) Layer the frozen chicken pieces into the Crock-Pot®.
2) Combine the preserves and chili sauce in a small container (a mixing cup is ideal). Empty it over the chicken. *Note:* You can also use pineapple or a combination.

3) Toss to mix and let the Pot do the work.
4) Enjoy with some veggies and rice.

Servings: Six (one cup per serving)

Cooking Time on the high setting is 2 to 3 hours.

Creamy Taco Chicken

Ingredients

1 Can Rotel Original Tomatoes with Green Chilies

3 chicken breasts (no bone or skin)

4-ounces cream cheese (regular or light)

Directions

1) Pour the tomatoes, and place the chicken into the slow cooker.
2) A few minutes before the end of the cooking cycle, use a fork or tongs to shred the chicken.
3) Put the cream cheese on top of the mixture, but don't stir.
4) By the time the meal is ready, the cheese will be oozing into your chicken. Yummy!

Suggestions: You can use this in a casserole, over rice, as a salad, or any other creative plan you may have for your meal.

Cooking Time: Low temperature - Six to Eight hours

Stuffed – Roasted Turkey

Ingredients

2 C. Stuffing Mix

Black pepper and salt

6 Pounds Turkey

1 Tablespoon melted butter

Instructions

1) Use the package instructions to prepare the stuffing.

2) Flavor the turkey with some melted butter, pepper, and salt.
3) Prepare the bird by loosely placing the stuffing in the carcass.
4) Cover and let the Pot do the rest.

Servings: Four

Cooking Time: Low: 9 to 11 hours; High: 5 hours

Fish

Citrus Flavored Fish

Ingredients

Pepper and Salt

1 ½ pounds fish fillets

1 medium chopped onion

4 tsp. oil

5 Tbsp. Chopped parsley

2 tsp. Each grated: lemon and orange rind

Garnish: Lemon and orange slices

Directions

Use some butter to grease the Crock-Pot®.

1) Flavor the fish with some pepper and salt and put it into the pot.
2) Add the parsley, grated rinds, and onion as well as the oil over the fish.
3) Cover and cook.
4) When ready to eat; garnish with some lemon or orange slices.

Cooking Time: 1 ½ Hours on Low

Salmon Bake

Ingredients

3 (one-pound) Cans Salmon

1 (16-ounces) can tomato puree

4 cups bread crumbs (10 slices worth)

1 chopped green pepper

3 teaspoons lemon juice

2 crushed chicken bouillon cubes

1 Can each (condensed) cream of onion soup & cream of celery soup

6 (well-beaten) eggs

½ cup milk

Directions

1) Use some cooking spray or other oil to grease the Crock-Pot® lightly.
2) Blend all of the ingredients—except for the milk and celery soup into the Pot.
3) Cover and cook.
4) Combine and stir the milk and celery soup in a small pan to use as a sauce for the salmon.
5) When the salmon is done, garnish and enjoy with the special sauce!

Cooking Time: High for three hours or low for four to six hours

Pork

BBQ Style Pork Steaks

Ingredients

4 (½-inch cut) Pork shoulder steaks

2 large sliced tomatoes

1 large onion

1 large thinly sliced bell pepper

1 Tbsp. Each:

- Vegetable oil
- Tapioca (quick-cooking)

¼ C. red wine

½ tsp. cumin

½ C. barbecue sauce (your choice)

Directions

1) Slice and cut the onion as if you are preparing to make onion rings for dinner.
2) Trim away an excess fat and slice the steaks in half - lengthwise.
3) Brown the steaks in skillet using hot oil, and drain on paper towels.
4) Organize the peppers, tomatoes, and onions in the Crock-Pot®; sprinkling the tapioca over them. Place the pork in last.
5) Prepare the cumin, wine, and barbecue sauce in a small dish. Pour it over the ingredients in the Pot, and cover.

Servings: Four

Cooking Time: Low Heat – Six to Eight Hours (or until veggies and meat are tender)

Note: The recipe is based on a 3 ½- or a 4-quart Crock-Pot®. If you have a different size the cooking time may vary.

Pepsi® Roast

Ingredients

1 Can Cream of mushroom soup

5 Lb. Pork Roast/ Steak/Chops

½ package dry onion soup mix

1 can Regular Pepsi (Don't use Diet)

Directions

1) Put the meat in the Crock-Pot® first and sprinkle with the soup mix.
2) Empty the mushroom soup and Pepsi over the meat.
3) Close the lid and let the pot do the rest of the chore.

Suggestion: Use the sauce to pour over some rice or potatoes.

Servings: Eight

Cooking Time: Low setting for six to seven hours

Ranch Chops

Ingredients

Pouch – Ranch Dressing Mix

Pork Chops

1 Can Cream of Chicken Soup Plus (+) 1 Can Water OR 2 Cups Cream of Chicken

Directions

1) Pour the liquids into the Crock-Pot® along with the chops and dressing mix.

Cooking Time: Use the low-temperature setting for four to six hours.

Ham in Cider Gravy

This ham is so tasty it cannot remain in the 'breakfast only' slot. It is so tasty and can advance to lunch and dinner menus as well.

Ingredients

1 (one to four pound) Ham

¾ cup maple syrup

2 cups unsweetened apple cider

3 Tablespoons cornstarch

Directions

1) Arrange the ham in the Crock-Pot® and top it off with the syrup and cider.
2) Cook until the time indicated below is completed.
3) Move the ham to a serving platter. Pour the liquid into a large cup (a measuring cup is perfect).
4) Whisk ½ of the cider and the cornstarch on the stovetop using the low-temperature setting until it is smooth. Continue whisking and increase the burner to med-low—adding small amounts of cider at a time—until the gravy is bubbly and thickened to the desired consistency.

Servings: Four to Eight

Preparation Time: Four minutes

Cooking Time: Low - six to eight hours

Casseroles

Crock-Pot® Dinner: Beef or Chicken

Ingredients

1 Whole/cut up chicken –or- legs and thighs OR a Beef Roast

2 Carrots

4 Potatoes

5 Ounces water

1 Can celery or cream of mushroom soup (10 ¾ ounce)

Directions

1) Cut the carrots into four-inch chunks. Put all of the ingredients into the Crock-Pot®.
2) Set the Pot and let it 'go.'

Servings: Four

Cooking Time: The high setting will cook the meal in six hours, or you can cook it all day using the low-temperature setting.

Squash 'N Chops

Ingredients

5 Pork (boneless) Port cutlets or chops

2 medium oranges

1 ¼ Pounds delicate/butternut squash

1/8 tsp. Ground red pepper

½ tsp. Garlic salt

¼ tsp. Each: Ginger, cloves, and cinnamon

Directions

1) Peel and slice the oranges. Peel and slice the squash lengthwise and discard the seeds. Cut the 'half' into sections ½-inches thick.
2) Flavor the pork with some garlic salt and red peppers. Use a 4- to 5- quart Crock-Pot® and place the chops/cutlets in the bottom.
3) Combine the ginger, cinnamon, and cloves in a small dish.
4) Top off the pork with the oranges along with the toppings in step 3.
5) Cover and cook.

Servings: 5

Cooking Time: Low for 4 hours

Lasagna Enchantment

This one has a few more steps, but it is so worth it—and it's easy.

Ingredients

2 Cans diced tomatoes (28-ounces) drained

Four finely chopped clove of garlic

2 Tbsp. oregano

½ tsp. salt

15-ounces fresh ricotta

¼ tsp. pepper

½ tsp. salt

½ C. shredded Parmesan cheese

1 (12-ounce) Package uncooked lasagna noodles

½ tsp. fresh (finely chopped) parsley – more if desired

2 C. spinach leaves (bagged is okay)

2 C. shredded Mozzarella cheese

Directions

1) Mix the garlic, drained tomatoes, pepper, salt, and oregano in a mixing container.
2) In another bowl, blend the parsley, Parmesan, and ricotta cheese.
3) Dip anywhere from 1/3 to ½ cup of the tomato combination on the base of the Crock-Pot®.
4) Layer the noodles, spinach, several dollops of the ricotta combo, and 1/3 to about ½ of the tomato combination. Sprinkle the mozzarella on the top of that section. Continue the process with the mozzarella on the top.
5) Close the lid on the Pot and let it do the work.

Servings: Six to Eight

Prep Time: 20 Minutes

Cook Time: High is 2 Hrs. or Low is 3 to 4 Hrs.

Sweet Potato Casserole

Ingredients

1 ½ C. applesauce

1 tsp. ground cinnamon

3 Tbsp. Margarine/butter

½ C. Toasted chopped nuts

2/3 C. Brown sugar

6 medium sweet potatoes

Directions

1) Peel and slice the potatoes cutting them into ½-inch bits and drop them into a 3 ½-quart Crock-Pot®.
2) In a separate dish, mix the brown sugar, cinnamon, melted butter, and applesauce. *Note*: Be sure you pack the brown sugar tight when it is measured.
3) Empty the mixture over the potatoes in the Pot.
4) When the potatoes are tender; you can top with the chopped nuts. Yummy!

Cooking Time: Six to Eight hours

Sides/Veggies

Slow Cooked Baked Potatoes

Ingredients

6 Baking Potatoes

Kosher Salt

Oil

Garnishes: Your choice

Directions

1) Prepare the potatoes with a good scrub and rinsing, but do not dry them.
2) Put each one in some foil while poking holes in each one using a fork.

3) Use a small amount of oil to drizzle over each one adding a sprinkle of salt, and close the foil.
4) To keep them from getting soggy, ball up several wads of foil into the cooker.
5) Layer the potatoes on the balls and cover. Leave them on warm in the Crock-Pot® until ready to serve.

Cooking Time: Low – Six to Eight Hours

Corn on the Cob

Ingredients

3 ears or 5 to 6 halves – Corn on the cob

Salt as needed

1/2 stick or ¼ cup of softened butter

Directions

1) Shuck and remove the silks from the corn; break them into halves.
2) Cover each one with butter and wrap individually in foil.
3) Wad some foil balls up in the base of the unit and add about 1-inch of water.
4) Put the potatoes into the Crock-Pot®, and cook for the allotted time.

Servings: 4

Preparation Time: Five minutes

Cooking Time: Use the high setting for two hours. *Note*: The cooking time may vary if you prepare the corn with another unit besides a 5 to 6-quart pot.

Ranch Mushrooms

Ingredients

½ Cup Melted butter

1 Pound fresh mushrooms

1 Package - ranch salad dressing mix

Instructions

1) Leave the mushrooms whole and wash them well.
2) Put them into the Crock-Pot®, adding the oil and ranch mix by drizzling it over the mushrooms.
3) Cover the Pot. It is best to stir once after hour one to blend the butter.

Servings: Six

Cooking Time: Low will have your mushrooms ready in three to four hours.

Sweet Potatoes

Ingredients

4 medium sweet potatoes

Optional Garnishes:

Brown Sugar, Butter, Mini Marshmallows

Directions

1) Clean and prepare the potatoes—thoroughly dry.
2) Use a fork and poke holes in each one, and double wrap them in aluminum foil.
3) Put them in the Crock-Pot®--cooking them the specified amount of time. If you are close to the kitchen; turn and flip the potatoes in the pot occasionally.
4) Once they are done, add the garnishes of your choice and serve.

Servings: Four

Preparation Time: Five Minutes

Cooking Time: The Low setting is used for 8 hrs. or the High setting for 4 hrs. (Times may vary depending on the size of the potatoes, but you will know when they are ready by how soft the potato is when you give it a squeeze.)

Chapter 5: Desserts – Snacks & Treats to Devour

Apple Dump Cake

Ingredients

Butter (1 Stick)

Yellow cake mix (1 box)

Apple pie filling (1 Can)

Directions

1) Empty the apple filling into the Crock-Pot®.
2) *Dump* in the mix and then the butter on top of the mix.

Cooking Time: Cook the cake in the Pot on the low setting for approximately four hours for best results.

Enjoy!

Applesauce

Ingredients

12 Apples

1 teaspoon juice (+) ¼ of the lemon peel

2 cinnamon sticks

Directions

1) Peel, core, and slice the apples. Put the apples, lemon peel, and sticks into the Crock-Pot®.
2) Provide a drizzle to the top with the juice and set the cooking timer.

3) When the treat is ready—throw the lemon peel and cinnamon sticks into the garbage.
4) Blend with a regular or immersion blender.
5) Chill for a few hours.

Cooking Time is five to seven hrs.

Peach Cobbler

Ingredients

1 White cake mix (not prepared)

6 Large peaches

1- Stick (½- Cup) softened butter

Directions

1) Peel and slice the peaches, and put them into the Crock-Pot®.
2) Blend the butter and cake mix using a pastry blender. You want a crumbly texture.
3) Sprinkle the mix over the peaches, and cook.

Enjoy with a bowl of ice cream.

Servings: Eight

Preparation Time: Fifteen minutes

Cooking Times on the high setting is two to three hours; whereas the Low cycle will extend for about four hours.

Cocktail Franks – Sweet and Sour

Ingredients

40- Ounces Pineapple chunks

2 Pounds cocktail franks

1 Cup each:

- Grape jelly

- Chili sauce

3 Tablespoons each:

- Prepared mustard
- Lemon juice

Directions

1) Mix the jelly, chili sauce, mustard, and lemon juice in the Pot, mixing it well.
2) Cover and use the high setting for fifteen to twenty minutes to blend the ingredients
3) Slice the franks into bite-sized pieces and add to the Crock-Pot®.
4) Pour in the drained chunks of pineapple.

Servings: 10

Cooking Times: *High* setting for two hours; *Low* setting for four hours.

Index for the Recipes

Chapter 2: Healthy Breakfast Recipes

Chicken & Turkey

- Buffalo Chicken
- Caesar Chicken
- Cranberry Chicken
- French Onion Chicken
- Hawaiian Chicken
- Honey Mustard Chicken
- Chicken Italian Style
- Swedish Meatballs
- Sweet and Sour Chicken
- Creamy Taco Chicken
- Stuffed – Roasted Turkey

Fish

- Citrus Flavored Fish
- Salmon Bake

Pork

- BBQ Style Pork Steaks
- Pepsi® Roast
- Ranch Chops
- Ham in Cider Gravy

Casseroles

- Crock-Pot® Dinner: Beef or Chicken
- Squash 'N Chops
- Lasagna Enchantment
- Sweet Potato Casserole

PART II

Chapter 1: What Clean Eating Is

So, you want to get healthy, feel better, maybe lose a few pounds, and you keep hearing about clean eating everywhere, right? Although at a glance, making the decision to clear your kitchen and eat clean may seem daunting, it doesn't have to be! I promise, clean eating is NOT. THAT. HARD. Before we look at what clean eating really means, let's discuss what it isn't. Clean eating is not:

- A diet. This is not a diet, or a quick fix to shed a few pounds.
- A torture mechanism. You are in no way going to be deprived of the food you love.
- A perfect practice. Clean eating is a journey, not a destination. Clean eating isn't an elitist gimmick or fad, it is a lifestyle change.

Now that you can breathe a little easier knowing that nobody is going to judge you, and that clean eating is not reserved for the perfect and always polished, let's talk about what clean eating really is.

Clean eating is about eliminating foods from your diet that aren't really foods at all, getting rid of foods and ingredients that have zero nutritional benefits, and getting back to basics. Food should feed our bodies, minds, and souls. Food should not be made in a laboratory, genetically toyed with, or leave our bodies unsatisfied and unhealthy. Food is fuel, but it should be fuel we share with our loved ones, enjoyed, and above all, good for us!

Let's Get Started

Where does one begin the journey to kicking the junk? Well, that really depends on how far you are willing to take things, and your comfort level. Everyone wants to look and feel better, and clean eating will help you achieve those goals. But, almost everything in your pantry and kitchen is full of stuff you do not need. Below is an idea of where to start cleaning up your diet for the better.

Kick the preservatives, chemicals, and processed food.

I know this seems daunting when you really consider what is on the grocery store shelves today, but you can start small. Chips are great and all, but check out that back label. Can you pronounce all the ingredients and do you know what they are? Are there more than 5 ingredients? Can you thinly slice potatoes and bake or broil them? If you answered no to all the above questions, you may starve. Just kidding! The point here is to really think about what is in those chips, and whether you are ready to either substitute them in your diet, or if it is easier to eliminate them all together. You can eat what you want, but do you really think those bagged chips are fueling your body in a healthy way considering the label?

Eliminate GMO foods wherever you can

And while chips are an easy target, consider the ears of corn at your local grocers. They are big, bright, and look really yummy, but so very bad. Most corn is genetically modified, so check the stickers, take note of the display, or ask an employee. Buying certified organic fresh produce is a great way to ensure that your food is GMO free. Organic does sometimes cost more, but buying seasonal produce from a local market is usually not any costlier than what you can get at major chain grocery stores. And, you are doing your local economy a huge favor. To start small, consider buying organic, and replacing your current selections of the notorious top ten listed below.

The top 10 genetically modified foods are:

- Soy
- Dairy Products
- Corn
- Rice
- Tomatoes
- Potatoes
- Canola
- Papaya
- Peas

The list above is a good place to start. The goal is to get clean, not stress yourself out. There is no shame in starting small and working your way from there. Any positive, healthy changes will have your body thanking you, Trust me.

Chapter 2: Benefits of Clean Eating

So, what are the benefits of eating clean? Consider that you are getting rid of foods that are not only lacking nutritional value, but that these foods also contain a varying array of toxins, poisons, and additives that can make you prone to illnesses that can literally kill you. Clean eating will eliminate the garbage, and fill your body with nutrient rich foods. Foods that are dense in nutrients help your body build and maintain a healthier gut, which in turn translates into a healthier, more effective immune system. You will not only be less likely to get sick, you will also be decreasing your chances of forming chronic illnesses, many of which are linked to the chemicals, preservatives, and GMO's that many people ingest daily.

Another awesome side effect of eating clean is that by eating cleaner, you are eating healthier. Most people that make the change report healthy, steady, weight loss, and that is a bonus for most of us! Eating clean foods chock full of nutrition, you will also feel fuller on less weight per average meal. Imagine a wrap that weighs 6 ounces filling you up better than a frozen pizza that weighs 16 ounces, and gives you more energy. Speaking of energy…

Eating clean will give you more energy, and your energy levels will maintain better throughout the course of the day. By eliminating empty carbohydrates, refined and sugar foods, and steering clear of refined grains, your body will begin regulate its insulin levels naturally. No spike in blood sugar equals no sugar crash later.

Clean eating also encourages an increase in Omega-3 fatty acids in your diet, which help your brain. B complex vitamins are good for your entire system, and increase serotonin and dopamine chemicals released by the brain, making you feel happier. And, Omega-3 fatty acids have been shown to reduce moodiness and even help decrease depression. Another benefit to eating clean is that you will sleep better too! Passing on a cookie and milk before bed and instead noshing on a handful of almonds (which contain tryptophan) and skim milk (that offers us melatonin) will help you sleep like a baby, and wake up refreshed. There are a thousand reasons why clean eating is good for you, and your body will only thank you!

PART III

Chapter 1

Breakfast Recipes

Hard Boiled Eggs

There is always a choice for breakfast if you have some boiled eggs at hands. You can cook two or as many as your pot will hold at one time. Check each one closely to be sure it is not cracked.

Directions

1) Empty one cup of water into the IP and place trivet inside the pot.

2) Put the eggs on the basket/trivet and tightly close the lid/vent valve.
3) Use the High pressure—manual setting:
    a) Five Minutes = Hard Boiled
    b) Four Minutes = Soft Boiled
    c) One Minute = Runny Yolk
4) Take the eggs from the pot and put them in cold water. After they are cool, you can place them in the refrigerator.

Instant Pot Oatmeal

Ingredients

1 cup of steel cut oats AND 3 cups of water

That is all!

Options: Cinnamon and apples

Directions

1) Place the water and oats into the pot.
2) Shut the lid and vent.
3) Use the manual buttons and arrows—setting the oats to cook for three minutes.
4) Unplug the pot and let the pressure to release naturally.
5) Open the lid and stir the oats.

Use the garnishes of your choice and enjoy this nutritional treat.

Yields: 2 to 3 servings

Instant Pot Creamy Coconut Style Steel-Cut Oats

Ingredients

1 cup coconut milk (plus more for the topping)

1 cup steel-cut oats

½ cup unsweetened coconut flakes

2 tablespoons brown sugar

2 cups water

A pinch of salt

Optional: ½ teaspoon ground cinnamon or 1 cinnamon stick

Directions

1) Toast the coconut. Add it to the IP using the sauté function at medium heat—frequently stirring to prevent scorching. When lightly browned, remove half of it and set it to the side for the topping. Add the oats to the toasting mixture.
2) Continue cooking the coconut and oats until you smell the aroma. Add one cup of the coconut milk—reserving the rest for the topping, and add the remainder of the ingredients.

3) Stir and set the cooker to high pressure for two minutes. You will need to click 'cancel' to stop the sauté function; close the lid and punch in the two minutes, manually.
4) When the time is completed, allow the pot to natural release before you open the valve and lid.
5) Drizzle with a sprinkle of coconut milk, a bit of the toasted coconut, and any other toppings to your liking.

Yields: 4 servings

Peach Cobbler Oatmeal

Ingredients

5 cups rolled oats

1 (14-ounce) can coconut cream

2 cups water

1 bag (8-ounces) frozen peaches

¼ C. brown sugar

Directions

1) Put all of the ingredients into the I P for seven minutes using the manual setting.
2) Quick release and enjoy.

Peach Crisp Compote

Ingredients

8 ripe chopped peaches

1 vanilla bean

2 to 3 Tbsp. each of white sugar and brown sugar

1 tsp. vanilla extract

2 Tbsp. Grape-nuts® Cereal (or more)

1 tsp. ground cinnamon

Optional: 1/4 cup of 5-grain oats

Directions

1) Blend the sugar, peaches, vanilla extract, vanilla bean, and cinnamon into the Instant Pot. Add oats if you want them
2) Close the pressure valve and lock the lid. Cook one minute on high pressure.
3) Allow ten minutes for the natural pressure release (NPR) after the beep sounds.
4) If you crave a syrupy compote; continue simmering until you have it at the consistency you want.
5) Add the Grape-nuts and blend.

Yields: 6 cups

Notes: It is so quick and easy. You can use this as a to fill turnovers, tarts, or just to spread over waffles or pancakes. You can also store some of it in canning jars for later.

Instant Pot Applesauce

Ingredients

3 Lbs. apples (your choice)

1 to 2 cinnamon sticks

Pinch of salt

¼ to ½ tsp. nutmeg

Sprinkle of honey to taste

Directions

1) Quarter the Apples.
2) Begin by pouring the water into the pot along with the three pounds of quartered apples.
3) Add the nutmeg and cinnamon sticks.
4) Close the lid and set the high pressure for five minutes.
5) Turn the heat off and allow natural release. Open the lid cautiously.
6) Remove the sticks, add the salt, and using an immersion blender, blend until you like the consistency. Sprinkle with a bit of honey.

IP Yogurt and Fruit

Ingredients

½ cup Greek yogurt

1-gallon milk

2 cups fruit

2 tablespoons vanilla bean paste

1 cup sugar

Directions

1) Pour the milk into the Instant Pot, secure the lid, and press the yogurt function.
2) Set the pot to the boil function which will beep in about 45 minutes.
3) Unplug the pot—removing the base and the lid—cool the milk until it reaches 115°F.
4) Place the base back with the IP and turn it on. Whisk the vanilla paste with the yogurt.
5) Click the yogurt function again with the timer set at 0:00.
6) Let it cook for up to eight hours. Use the napkins or nut bags and strain the yogurt
7) Put it into one-quart jars and chill overnight in the refrigerator.

8) Boil the sugar and two cups of fruit. Cool the mixture before you add it to the yogurt.

9) Place into smaller containers with a dab of fruit on the bottom and top.

Note: You can use ½ gallon whole milk and ½ gallon 2% if you wish.

Equipment Needed:

- One-quart jars Cooking Thermometer
- Cloth napkins or nut milk bags

Apple Bread with Salted Caramel Icing

Ingredients

3 cups apples

2 eggs

1 cup sugar

1 tablespoon apple pie spice

2 cups all-purpose flour

1 tablespoon vanilla

1 tablespoon baking powder

1 stick butter

For the Topping:

1 cup heavy cream

2 cups brown sugar

2 cups powdered sugar

1 stick butter

Directions

1) Peel, core, and cube the apples.
2) Using a mixer, blend the butter, eggs, pie spice, and sugar—mixing until smooth and creamy. Pour in the apples.
3) In a separate dish, blend the baking powder and flour. Combine the mixture with the wet ingredients in portions. The batter will be thick.
4) Pour the mixture into a seven-inch spring-form pan.
5) Put the trivet into the IP and add a cup of water.
6) Place the pan in the pot and use the manual setting for 70 minutes on high pressure. Do QR and remove the bread.
7) *Make the Icing*: Melt the butter and brown sugar together in a small saucepan, usually about three minutes. Stir in the cream and continue cooking for around two or three minutes. Take it from the stovetop and let it cool completely. Mix in the powdered sugar, blending until there are no lumps.
8) Top the bread with the icing.

Chapter 2

Lunch Recipes

Lentil Tacos

You can use these as a crunchy or soft taco or part of burrito salad!

Ingredients

4 cups water

2 cups dry brown lentils

4 ounces tomato sauce

½ teaspoon cumin

1 teaspoon each:

- Onion powder

- Chili powder
- Salt
- Garlic powder

Directions

1) Begin by placing all of the ingredients into the IP. Thoroughly stir.
2) Close the lid and be sure you have it sealed.
3) Using the manual function button and arrows, set the timer on the pot for 15 minutes. Turn the IP off and release the pressure.
4) Open the pot carefully and stir. Let it rest for a few minutes, and then enjoy your lunch.

Broth—Soups—& Stews

IP Bone Broth

Boiling bones has been done for generations. You can use turkey, chicken pigs, or any other meat for the base. You can also make some for now and some for later. It can be either frozen or placed into canning jars.

Instructions for the Bones:

- Roast the bones at 400°F for approximately 45 minutes if they have been stored in the freezer.

Ingredients

1 to 2 tablespoons of apple cider vinegar

1 medium onion

1 to 2 large carrots

1 head smashed garlic

2 to 3 stalks of celery

Water to cover the bones

Optional: 1 to 2 chicken feet (gel for the broth)

Directions

1) Place the cooked bones into the pot before adding the garlic, vegetables, and vinegar
2) Add just enough water to cover the bones.
3) Allow the pot to sit for thirty minutes to absorb the bone minerals.
4) Turn the vent valve to the closed position when you place the top on the bones.
5) Turn on the soup function and set the manual time button for 120 minutes.
6) The IP will instantly turn on. It will take around twenty minutes before you begin the countdown. After the time is up, turn the

pot off and wait for the natural release in about fifteen minutes before trying to open the vent.

7) Strain the broth.

Note: If you choose to use the chicken feet; ask an ethnic store or a farmer's market or ask your local grocery store if they can be ordered. The feet are full of collagen, and many trace essential minerals.

Cheesy Broccoli Cream Soup

Ingredients

4 cups (or more) vegetable broth

1 head trimmed broccoli florets

3 minced garlic cloves

Pepper and Salt

1 chopped onion

1 tablespoon olive oil

3 chopped carrots

12 ounces Velveeta cheese

½ cup heavy cream

Directions

1) Using the sauté button, pour the oil into the IP and toss in the onions. Sauté until the onion is soft. Throw in the garlic and continue cooking for approximately 30 seconds.
2) Mix in the carrots, broccoli, and the broth.
3) Put the lid on the Instant Pot securely and cook six minutes on the high-pressure setting. Turn the unit off and use the QR to release the pressure.
4) For the meantime, use an immersion blender or potato masher to prepare the soup.
5) Add the cheese and salt. Use some pepper and salt for additional flavoring.

Chicken and Lentil Soup

Ingredients

3 (12-ounce) skinless and boneless chicken thighs

1 pound dried lentils

2 Tbsp. Chicken 'Better than Bouillon'

7 cups water

2 chopped scallions

1 small chopped onion

¼ cup chopped cilantro

1 medium diced ripe tomato

3 garlic cloves

1 teaspoon garlic powder

¼ teaspoon oregano

½ teaspoon kosher salt (more or less)

1 teaspoon cumin ½ teaspoon paprika

Directions

1) Place all of the ingredients into the Instant Pot, cover, and cook for 30 minutes on the 'soup' function.
2) When the pressure releases, shred the chicken and mix well.

Yields: About 11 cups

Goat Stew With Taro

Ingredients

1 pound young goat meat

2 cups eddoes/taro

Animal fat or avocado oil (only enough to have a layer on the pot)

1 tablespoon coconut oil

1 small onion

4 garlic cloves (smashed)

1 cup bone broth (*Chapter 2*)

1 leek or 3 green onions

Sea salt

1 cup coconut milk

1 tablespoon coriander leaves

Directions

1) Cut the taro into one-inch chunks. Peel and dice the onion, and cut the goat into one-inch cubes. If you use the leek; use the white part and cut it into ½ -inch rings or cut the onions into one-inch long pieces.
2) Pour a layer of oil in the bottom of a skillet, fry the taro until crispy. Drain on some paper towels and set to the side.
3) Set the Instant Pot on the sauté function. Use the tablespoon of oil and add the onions. Remove them when translucent, and set aside in another container.
4) In batches, place the meat into the cooker until seared evenly. Top off with a small amount of olive oil if needed. Remove the meat and set it to the side.
5) Stir in the bone broth and remove the bits of meat with a wooden spoon. Combine the onions, meat, leeks or onions, and garlic. Cover the IP lid and set the valve to sealing.

6) Cook under the manual setting for 20 minutes. After the time has lapsed; press the cancel button and let it naturally cool until all pressure is released.
7) Select the sauté function, and combine the coconut milk, and taro chunks while gently stirring.
8) Add the desired amount of sea salt for flavoring. Let it simmer until the gravy thickens slightly—about five minutes.
9) Garnish with some chopped coriander.

Yields: Serves 4

Instant Pot Saag

This is an Indian version of creamed spinach dish that is full of many nutrients. It is even better the second day.

Ingredients

1 Lb. rinsed mustard leaves

1 Lb. rinsed spinach

2 medium carrots

2 medium diced onions

4 minced garlic cloves

2-inch knob minced ginger

2 Tbsp. Ghee

2 tsp. salt

1 tsp. each: cumin, garam masala, & coriander

Pinch of dried fenugreek leaves (kasoori methi)

½ tsp. each: black pepper, turmeric, & cayenne

Directions

1) Use the sauté function button to melt the ghee using the Instant Pot.
2) Add the ginger, garlic, onion, and other spices to the pot while stirring for two to three minutes.
3) Add the spinach, and continue to stir the ingredients. When the spinach wilts; add the mustard greens.
4) Push in the 'keep warm/cancel' button; place the lid on and press the poultry function for fifteen minutes.
5) Once the IP pressure releases; add the mixture into a blender and mix to the desired consistency.
6) Return it to the pot and push the keep warm function until you are ready to serve dinner.
7) Garnish with a spoonful of ghee.

Notes: More ghee will be needed for serving. You may also want to add a small amount of corn or potato starch to thicken the soup. Use a small amount of the saag in a bowl and add the starch, mixing until it is dissolved. Pour it back into the sagg and blend it in well.

Sandwiches

French Dipped Roast Beef Sandwich

Ingredients

4 Lbs. beef roast

1 tsp. beef bouillon granules

¾ cup soy sauce

2 tsp. black peppercorns

1 tsp. minced garlic cloves

1 Tbsp. dried rosemary

For Serving: 8 white hamburger buns

Directions

1) Cut most of the fat away from the roast and place the roast into the inner pot.
2) Blend the peppercorns, bouillon, soy sauce, garlic, and rosemary.
3) Pour the mixture into the pot along with enough water to immerse the roast.
4) Lock the lid and close the steam nozzle—set the timer for 35 minutes on high.

5) Release the pressure and shred the roast.

Yields: 8 Servings

Sandwiches Pulled Barbecue

Choose the cut of beef and barbecue sauce you like to use for your friends and family.

Ingredients

4 cups cabbage

1 Tbsp. mustard

1/3 cup Worcestershire sauce

2 pounds beef

2 cups water

1 Tbsp. horseradish

½ cup BBQ sauce

1 cup ketchup

Directions

1) Finely shred the cabbage.
2) Blend all of the ingredients into the IP and place it on the 'meat' setting for 35 minutes.
3) Let the steam disperse, and remove the lid.

4) Use a fork to shred the beef. Return the meat to the sauce until it cooks down some using the sauté setting.

Beef Italian

Ingredients

2 while bay leaves

¼ tsp. black pepper

3 ½ pounds beef roast

1 Tbsp. wine vinegar

1 (16-ounce) can whole tomatoes

¼ cup water

1 tsp. salt

3 ½ tsp. minced garlic cloves

2 tsp. beef bouillon granules

½ tsp. pickling spice

Directions

1) Remove all of the fat and cut the beef to fit the inner pot.
2) Put everything else on top of the meat.
3) Lock the lid down, and seal the steaming nozzle.
4) Set the pot manually for 35 minutes or choose the meat-stew setting.

5) Use NR for five minutes the QR the rest of the pressure.

6) Take the bay leaf out, and serve with a side of mashed potatoes.

Yields: 4 servings

Pasta and Rice Side Dishes

Whole Wheat Spinach and Pasta

Ingredients

5 cups water

1 pound whole wheat fusilli pasta

4 minced garlic cloves (to taste)

4 cups chopped, frozen spinach

4 tablespoons butter (cubed)

Pepper and salt as desired

½ cup grated Parmesan cheese

Garnish: More parmesan cheese

Directions

1) Pour the water into the Instant Pot along with the pasta, garlic, with the frozen spinach on the top layer.

2) Set the pot using the high, manual function for six minutes. Quick release and open the top; add the butter, Parmesan cheese, pepper, and salt.

3) Place the top back on the IP, close, and allow the pasta to absorb the juices for about five minutes.
4) Garnish with more Parmesan cheese.

Yields: 8 servings

Red Beans and Rice

This is easy to prepare since there is no presoaking involved!

Ingredients

1 diced bell pepper

3 diced celery stalks

1 medium diced onion

3 minced garlic cloves

1 teaspoon salt

1 pound dry red kidney beans

½ teaspoon black pepper

Optional: ¼ teaspoon white pepper

1 teaspoon fresh thyme or ½ teaspoon dried

1 teaspoon hot sauce (Texas Pete)

2 bay leaves

7 cups water

10 cups cooked rice

1 pound chicken andouille (smoked) sausage (thinly sliced)

Directions

1) Blend all of the products except for the rice and sausage into the Instant Pot.
2) Close the lid and lock it, setting it to high pressure manually for 28 minutes.
3) Use the quick release. When the pressure is removed, take off the lid.
4) Add the sausage and return the lid back on the IP, and lock it down.
5) Manually set the IP for 15 minutes using high pressure. Let the pot naturally release.
6) Let the bean mixture set for a few minutes to make the liquid a little thicker.
7) Enjoy them over the bed of cooked rice.

Yields: 10 servings

Chapter 3

Dinner Recipes

Beef

Maple Smoked Brisket

Ingredients

1 ½ pound beef brisket

2 teaspoons smoked sea salt

2 tablespoons date sugar, maple sugar, or coconut sugar

1 teaspoon each:

- onion powder
- mustard powder
- black pepper

2 cups bone broth or your choice of stock

½ teaspoon smoked paprika

3 fresh thyme sprigs 1 tablespoon liquid smoke

Directions

1) Take the beef from the refrigerator, so it will be room temperature— about thirty minutes before cooking. Use two paper towels to pat it dry, and set it to the side.
2) Combine the spices by mixing the pepper, smoked sea salt, maple sugar, smoked paprika, onion powder, and mustard powder. Rub the mix on all sides of the brisket.

3) Set the IP on the sauté setting for two to three minutes.
4) Lightly grease the bottom of the cooker with a bit of oil and put the brisket into the pot.
5) Continue to sauté until all sides are browned. Turn the brisket with the fatty side up and add the thyme, liquid smoke, and broth. Be sure to scrape the bottom for the browned pieces.
6) Change the setting manually for 50 minutes, allowing the pot to release on its own. (The quick release may leave the meat dry.)
7) Remove it from the pot and cover it with some aluminum foil to rest.
8) Turn on the sauté function, and for about ten minutes allow the sauce to thicken.

Balsamic Beef Roast

Ingredients

1 teaspoon each:

- garlic powder
- black ground pepper

3 Lbs. boneless chuck roast

1 Tbsp. kosher salt

2 cups water

¼ cup balsamic vinegar

½ cup chopped onion

¼ tsp. xanthan gum

Garnish: Parsley

Directions

1) Cut the roast into two pieces.
2) Flavor the roast with the garlic powder, pepper, and salt on each side of the roast.
3) Using the sauté feature, brown both sides. Pour in one cup of water, the vinegar, and onion with the meat.
4) Cover and seal the IP and cook for 35 minutes.
5) When the time is done, free up the pressure and carefully remove the meat and place in a large container. Remove the fat and break the roast meat into chunks.
6) Using the sauté function, bring the remainder of the liquid to a boiling and simmer for ten minutes.
7) Whip in the xanthan gum and place the meat in the pot; stirring gently.
8) Turn the pot off and garnish with plenty of chopped parsley.

Spiced Cranberry Pot Roast

Ingredients

3 to 4 pounds arm roast (part of the chuck)

2 Tbsp. olive oil

1 cup whole cranberries (frozen or fresh)

1 (3-inch) cinnamon stick

Pinch of salt and pepper

¼ cup honey

½ cup of water

1 tsp. horseradish powder

6 whole cloves

2 large garlic cloves

2 cups bone broth (See *Chapter 2 Soups*)

Optional: ½ cup white wine or ½ cup more of the broth

Directions

1) Remove the skin from the clove but leave it whole.
2) Use two paper towels to pat the roast dry and flavor with some pepper and salt.
3) Set the IP on the sauté function to brown the roast from eight to ten minutes. Take it out and set it aside.

4) Empty the wine into the pot. Use a wooden spoon to remove the pieces from the base of the pot. Continue cooking for about four or five minutes, still scraping the pot.
5) Pour in the horseradish powder, whole cloves, honey, the cinnamon stick, water, cranberries, and garlic. Cook for another four to five minutes constantly stirring until the cranberries split open.
6) Place the meat back into the Instant Pot, adding enough broth to bring the level to almost cover the meat.
7) Lock the lid and set the timer for 75 minutes using high pressure, turn it off, letting the pressure release naturally for about fifteen minutes.
8) Use the quick release the remainder of the pressure from the Instant Pot.
9) Place the meat into the serving dish and pour some of the sauce over the top as a garnish. Put the remainder of the sauce in a dish to use for serving.

Yields: 4 to 6 servings

Paleo Mongolian Beef

Ingredients

1 ½ Lbs. sliced flank steak

¼ C. Arrowroot

½ C. grated carrot

¾ C. honey ¾ C. water

¾ C. Coconut Aminos

2 Tbsp. olive oil

½ tsp. fresh ginger

1/3 C. scallion (green onion)

Directions

1) Peel and minced the ginger. Cover the steak with the arrowroot powder.
2) Mix the honey, water, coconut aminos, ginger, olive oil, green onions, and carrots; add to the inner pot.
3) Lock the lid and seal the steam nozzle. You can manually set the IP for 35 minutes or use the meat-stew function.
4) Naturally release the pressure for five minutes and QR the remainder of the pressure.

Yields: 1 cup

Spicy Orange Beef

Ingredients

2 pounds flank steak

(¼-inch strips)

2 bell peppers

6 minced cloves of garlic

1 tablespoon avocado oil

¼ cup organic tamari or coconut aminos

2 teaspoons sesame oil

¾ cup orange juice

½ teaspoon red pepper flakes

2 tablespoons arrowroot powder or cornstarch

1 teaspoon orange zest

1 bunch chopped green onions

3 tablespoons cold water

Directions

1) Remove the seeds and stems from the peppers and slice them into thin strips. Mince the garlic. Set it to the side.
2) Flavor the steak with pepper and salt. Slice up the steak into ¼-inch strips.

3) Add the oil to the Instant Pot and choose the sauté function. Brown the meat a little at a time in batches. Place the cooked steak in a container and set it to the side.
4) Add the garlic to the pot and cook for one minute; add the soy sauce, orange juice, orange zest, sesame oil, and red pepper flakes. Blend in the beef and juices.
5) Use the high-pressure setting for twelve minutes. When you hear the timer sound off on the Instant Pot; turn off the pot and use the QR.
6) Combine the bell peppers to the pot along with the water and cornstarch or arrowroot; whisk until smooth. Add the mix to the pot—constantly stirring. Select the sauté function and continue to cook until the sauce thickens
7) Toss in the diced green onions and serve right away over rice. Garnish with the red pepper flakes, green onion, and orange zest.

Yields: Serves 4

Chicken

Buttermilk Herb Chicken

Ingredients

2 Lbs. boneless breast of chicken

1 Tbsp. Dijon mustard

1 C. buttermilk

1 Tbsp. honey

1 tsp. each:

- salt
- dried thyme
- dried rosemary
- sage
- black pepper

Directions

1) Place all of the ingredients into a freezer bag and marinate for a minimum of one hour in the refrigerator.
2) Place the breasts and marinade into the cooker; lock and seal the steam nozzle.
3) Set the timer for fifteen minutes or select the poultry setting.
4) Naturally release the pressure for about five minutes; QR the remainder of the pressure.

Yields: 4 servings

Chicken Balsamic Chicken with Mushrooms and Pears

Ingredients

4 Lbs. boneless breast of chicken

1 (37.5-ounce) can sliced pears

½ tsp. sea salt

1 Tbsp. light brown sugar

1/3 balsamic vinegar

1 tsp. ground black pepper

Directions

1) Blend all of the ingredients in the IP except for the mushrooms and pears.
2) Lock the lid and seal the nozzle for steam; manually set the timer for ten minutes. Release the pressure. Toss in the mushrooms and pears and lock the lid, and set the seal— manually set for five minutes.
3) Naturally release the pressure for five minutes and QR the remainder of the pressure.
4) Remove the top and sauté for five minutes to acquire a thicker sauce— depending on your preference.

Yields: 8 servings with ½ cup of sauce and 8 ounces of chicken.

IP Chicken Cordon Blue Casserole

Ingredients

1 (16-ounce) package Rotini pasta

1 pound boneless & skinless chicken breast

1 pound cubed ham

8 ounces Gouda cheese

16 ounces Swiss Cheese

8 ounces heavy cream

2 tablespoons butter

1 tablespoon spicy mustard

1 cup panko breadcrumbs

Directions

1) Cut the chicken into strips and cube the ham. Chop or shred the cheese.
2) Pour the uncooked pasta into the IP and cover with the chicken broth.
3) Put the ham and chicken strips on top.
4) Place the setting to 25 minutes using the manual high-pressure function. You can also use the poultry function. Quick release the pressure.
5) Pour in the heavy cream while stirring. Add both of the cheeses and mustard to the IP, stirring until the mixture is creamy.

6) Melt the butter in a small saucepan, and add the breadcrumbs. Sauté about two to three minutes or until golden.
7) Drizzle this onto the cordon blue and enjoy!

Curried Lemon Instant Pot Coconut Chicken

Ingredients

4 Lbs. chicken (any type)

¼ cup lemon juice

1 Can regular coconut milk

1 Tbsp. turmeric

½ tsp. salt

1 Tbsp. curry powder

Optional: ½ to 1 tsp. lemon zest

Directions

1) Combine the spices, and lemon juice, and milk in a bowl. (Leave out the chunk of coconut—if there was one—for now)
2) Pour a nominal amount of the combination into the Instant Pot and add the chicken.
3) Pour the balance of the ingredients, along with the chunk of coconut cream (if there was one) on the top of the pieces of chicken.

4) Close and lock the valve to the instant pot.
5) Set it for the poultry setting and let it go for about fifteen minutes under high- pressure. It may take twenty minutes to reach its pressure point.
6) After the fifteen minute cook time; open the valve with the QR.
7) Cut and check the center of the chicken for doneness. If it is still pink, allow additional six or eight minutes using the manual high-pressure setting.
8) Shred the chicken while in the pot with two forks. You can also move it to a plate to cut if it is easier for you.
9) Add the lemon zest after you have cooked the chicken.

Serve with rice or steamed/roasted veggies.

Salsa Verde Chicken

Ingredients

2 to 2½ pounds chicken breasts (boneless)

16 ounces salsa Verde

1 teaspoon each: Kosher salt, Smoked Paprika, & Cumin

Directions

1) Combine all of the ingredients in the IP, setting the pressure on high for 25 minutes.

2) Use the quick release when the timer goes off.

3) Shred the chicken using two forks.

Pork

Pork Shoulder Carnitas

Ingredients for the Shoulder

4-pound pork shoulder

5 garlic cloves

2 cups chicken stock

1 teaspoon Himalayan Pink Salt

½ cup onion

¼ teaspoon ground black pepper

2 cups shredded lettuce

8 whole tortillas or large lettuce leaves

2 cups *Easy Avocado Salsa Easy Avocado Salsa*

Ingredients for the Salsa

1 tablespoon minced red onion

2/3 cup tomatoes (seeded and diced)

1 tablespoon lime juice (fresh squeezed)

1 Pinch of Himalayan Pink Salt

½ cup cilantro (packed—roughly chopped)

1 tablespoon minced jalapeno

¼ teaspoon ground fresh black peppercorns

1 cup diced avocado

Directions for Salsa:

1) Blend all of the ingredients in a medium container. Begin with the tomato, lime juice, onion, and cilantro.
2) Flavor the mixture with pepper, jalapeno, and salt.
3) Add the avocado; stir and serve!
4) *Note*: You can use about one large Roma tomato.

Directions for the Carnitas:

1) Place the shoulder and water in the Instant Pot. Add the onions, cloves, and sprinkle the flavorings of salt and pepper to the top of the pork.
2) Lock the cooker and set it for 45 minutes on high pressure (more or less depending on the size of the shoulder).

Make the tacos:

1) Warm the tortillas using medium heat.
2) Place a layer of lettuce, the carnitas, and top off with the homemade salsa.

Pork IP Honey Pork Chops

Ingredients

2 pounds boneless pork chops

¼ tsp. ground cloves

1/2 Tbsp. maple syrup

¼ tsp. black pepper

½ tsp. cinnamon

½ tsp. fresh ginger

2 Tbsp. Dijon mustard

½ tsp. sea salt

¼ cups honey

Directions

1) Use the salt and pepper to flavor the chops and place them into the inner pot.
2) Peel and mince the ginger.
3) Turn on the sauté function and brown each side.
4) In a separate dish; add the maple syrup, honey, Dijon mustard, cloves, cinnamon, and ginger. Pour the mixture over the chops—lock the lid—and seal the steam nozzle.
5) Manually set the dial to the Instant Pot for fifteen minutes.

6) Use the natural release the pressure off of the chops in the pot for five minutes. Then, quick release the remainder of the pressure.

Pork Smoked Chops with Split Pea Soup

Ingredients

15 ounces (about 2 cups) pork chops

6 whole Allspice

3 cardamom pods

1 cup each chopped:

- onion
- carrot
- 1 star anise
- 1 bay leaf

½ pound ham hock

3 chopped garlic cloves

½ tsp. each:

- ground cumin
- salt 1 tsp. each:
- black pepper

- dried thyme
- grated orange rind

¼ cup each:

- dry sherry
- orange juice

7 cups water

Note: This delicious soup is much easier to prepare if you use an immersion blender and a Dutch oven.

Directions

1) Trim and dice the chops.
2) Prepare the beans by sorting and washing; put them in the Dutch oven.
3) Put the star anise, cardamom pods, and allspice on doubled cheesecloth. Grasp the edges and tie them together and toss into the IP.
4) Also, toss in the onion, peas, and rest of ingredients except for the chops and orange rind.
5) Close and securely lock the lid to the pot. Put the steam release to the 'venting' position. Press the slow-cook button, and adjust to select the 'less' mode to five hours of cooking time.

6) At the end of that time; take off the lid and add the pork. Close and relock the lid of the IP for three hours. (Cook until done.)

7) Take the lid off; throw away the ham hock, spice bag, and bay leaf.

8) Put ½ of the soup into a blender—removing the center of the lid— and continue to mix until it is creamy smooth. Return this to the soup and blend in the rind.

Yields: 8 servings

Sides and Vegetables

Pressure-Steamed Artichokes

Ingredients

2 Medium whole artichokes (About 5.5 ounces)

1 cup of water 1 lemon wedge

Directions

1) Discard the damaged leaves and wash the artichokes. Remove the stem and top off 1/3 of each artichoke. Rub each one with a lemon wedge to prevent them from browning too quickly.

2) Place the rack into the IP trivet insert and put the artichokes on top. Add the water and close the lid making sure the valve is in the sealed position.

3) Set the manual mode time for 20 minutes.
4) Hit cancel at the end of 20 minutes to turn off the warming function.
5) Wait approximately ten minutes, and open the valve to release the pressure.

Yields: Two to four servings

Mashed Acorn Squash

Ingredients

2 acorn squash (trimmed stem, halved, seeded)

1 tsp. kosher salt

¼ tsp. baking soda

½ C. water Salt and pepper to taste

2 Tbsp. brown sugar

½ tsp. grated nutmeg

2 Tbsp. butter

Directions

1) Flavor the outside of the squash with some salt and baking soda.
2) Place the cooling rack or steaming basket in the pot with the water, positioning the squash on top. Close the lid and start the high-pressure setting, and cook for 20 minutes.

3) Quick release and remove the acorn squash from the Instant Pot. Remove the squash and let it cool. When cooled, remove the skin.
4) Mix in the brown sugar, butter, and nutmeg. Use a potato masher to blend until the squash is smooth.

Yields: 4 to 6 servings

Quick and Easy Baked Potatoes

Prepare as many or as few as you wish— up to five pounds.

Directions

1) Chop or peel the potatoes all the same size.
2) Place the steamer rack into the IP with one cup of water. Toss the potatoes into the pot. Close the lid and be sure it is sealed.
3) Using the manual button; set the time to ten minutes. After about twenty minutes; the pressure will naturally release.

Note: If you prefer a crispy crust you can also bake them at 350°F for about ten minutes.

IP Perfect Rice

All you need for this is one cup of water and one cup of Jasmine rice but can add more if you adjust the water accordingly.

Directions

1) Scrub the rice gently using cold water and discard the water; continue rinsing until the water remains clear.
2) Add the water and rice to the Instant Pot. Close the lid and cook three minutes using high pressure.
3) Use the natural release for ten minutes; release the remaining pressure and open the lid.
4) For additional flavoring, you can add some salt and fluff with a fork.

Cilantro Lime Brown Rice

Ingredients

2 cups water (or proportions according to the label instructions)

1 cup uncooked brown basmati rice

Juice of ½ Lime

¼ teaspoon salt (more or less to taste)

1 ½ Tablespoons butter

¼ cup chopped cilantro

Optional: ½ cup frozen corn kernels

Directions

1) Add the water and rice to the IP. Close the lid and cook three minutes using high pressure.

2) Use the natural release for 10 minutes; release the remaining pressure and open the lid.
3) Add the corn, lime juice, butter, and cilantro.
4) Serve right away.

Yields: 6 servings

Mexican Green Rice

Ingredients

1 ¼ cups low- sodium chicken or vegetable broth

Flesh of ½ avocado

1 cup of uncooked long grain ride

¼ Cup green hot sauce or green salsa

½ cup fresh cilantro Pinch of salt and pepper if you wish

Directions

1) Place the rice and broth into the Instant Pot—stir—and lock it down choosing the high-pressure cycle for three minutes.
2) After the beep; turn the cooker off and allow the ten-minute natural pressure release. After that, do a quick release. Fluff it with a fork.
3) In a blender, combine the salsa, cilantro, and avocado with a little water making it with a sour cream consistency.

4) Stir the rice into the mixture and add some pepper and salt for additional flavoring.

Yields: 3 cups

IP Tomato-less Sauce Pizza

Ingredients for the Sauce

½ cup chopped onion

3 beets (peeled and cut into rough chunks)

2 Tbsp. each:

- Chopped fresh basil
- Balsamic vinegar
- Apple cider vinegar

1 tsp. crushed garlic

1 Tbsp. dried oregano

1/8 tsp. salt

Directions for the Sauce

1) Place all of the sauce ingredients into the IP. Set for six minutes using the high- pressure manual function. After the time is complete, turn off the pot
2) Release the pressure by sliding the release to vent. Open the lid.

3) Using your blender or processor, mix until your sauce is the desired consistency.
4) Add to your crust.

Ingredients for the Crust

2/3 cup tapioca flour

2 green plantains (1/2 inch slices)

¼ cup coconut flour

1/8 tsp. salt

1 tsp. baking soda

1 Tbsp. melted palm shortening (divided)

1 Tbsp. each:

- Italian seasoning
- Garlic powder
- Nutritional yeast (*optional*)

Directions for the Crust

1) Preheat the oven to 400°F. Cut the parchment paper and line the pan or pizza stone.
2) Process the (very green) plantains in the food processor until creamy smooth. Toss in the tapioca flour and process for approximately thirty seconds.

3) Blend in the baking soda, coconut flour and half of the palm shortening in the processor; processing for thirty seconds.
4) Toss in the remainder of the ingredients except for the other half of the palm shortening to the processor. Process the mixture for an additional thirty seconds to form the pizza dough.
5) Form a ball using your hands and place it on the parchment-lined stone or pan. Press it outwards until you have your pizza crust shaped.
6) Brush the rest of the shortening over the crust and bake for ten minutes in the oven.
7) Take it from the oven and add the toppings. Cook for ten to twelve minutes.

Utensils Required:

- High-powered blender or immersion blender
- Food Processor
- Baking pan or Pizza stone
- Parchment Paper

Yields: Crust: One 12-inch pizza sauce: Two 12-inch pizzas

Chapter 4

Thanksgiving, Christmas, And New Year's Day Recipes

Breakfast Pumpkin Butter

Ingredients

1 cup apple juice

4 teaspoons pumpkin pie spice

2 cans pure pumpkin

½ cup sugar

Optional: 1 teaspoon ground ginger

Directions

1) Put each of the ingredients directly into the Instant Pot.
2) Use the high pressure for three minutes.
3) Allow the butter cool for at least three hours.
4) You can place the cooled product in whatever glass jars you might have in the cabinet. Use a marker to date each of them, and store them in the refrigerator.

Lunch or Dinner

Chicken and Turkey Chicken the Whole Bird for a Perfect Bird Every Time

Ingredients

1 whole chicken

1 tablespoon coconut oil

1 cup water

Season as you like

Directions

1) Place the steam rack inside of the pot and add the water.
2) Use a large skillet to preheat the oil.
3) Flavor the chicken with your desired seasonings and place in the skillet sear for one minute per side. Remove from the heat.
4) Put the chicken on the rack of the IP. Use high-pressure setting and alter the cooking time.

Cooking Time: 6 minutes per pound and add two minutes to the total time. For example, if you have a 8 pound chicken: 8 x 6 = 48 + 2 = 50 minutes.

Stuffing for the Bird

Ingredients

1 ¼ cups turkey or chicken broth

1 chopped onion

1 loaf sourdough bread (toasted, cubed, &cooled)

1 cup chopped celery

½ teaspoon each of salt and pepper

6 tablespoons butter

1 teaspoon poultry seasoning

Optional: ½ pound cooked ground sausage

Equipment Needed: Six-cup Bundt pan and a skillet

Directions

1) In a separate skillet; simmer the broth, onion, celery, butter, and spices until tender.
2) Using a separate bowl, pour the broth over the bread—blending well.
3) Pour the ingredients into the mixing bowl, and combine.
4) Use a small amount of cooking spray on a Bundt pan, and add the mixture. Cover with foil placing a hole in the center.
5) Pour 1 ½ cups of water into the IP, center the trivet, and place the pan inside using an aluminum foil sling to remove the stuffing later pan later.
6) Place the lid on—lock it, and set to high pressure for fifteen minutes.
7) Once you hear the beep, release the pressure and remove and remove the stuffing from the pan.

8) You can place it in a preset oven at 350°F for a few minutes to receive a crispy appearance.

Instant Pot Chicken and Sweet Potatoes

Ingredients

16 ounces diced sweet potatoes

1 pound chicken breast

3 tablespoons buffalo sauce

3 tablespoons butter

1 diced onion

½ teaspoon (less or more) each: onion and garlic powder

Directions

1) Turn on the Instant Pot sauté function.
2) Place the onion with one tablespoon of the butter into the IP; sauté until browned.
3) Toss in the sweet potatoes, chicken, buffalo sauce, and the remainder of the butter to the pot.
4) Close the top securely and set to the 'poultry' feature. (You will need to cook frozen chicken thirty minutes—set the time with the manual function.)

5) Once the poultry function is complete; quick release the vent and serve.

Note: If you like a thicker sauce; you can add one tablespoon of arrowroot—set back in the IP, and stir until it reaches the desired consistency.

Duck

Sous vide (Duck Breast)

This is a perfect recipe for two on the holiday.

Ingredients Step 2:

2 large boneless duck breasts (about 1.1 Lbs. or 480 grams)

2 teaspoons freshly minced garlic

1 teaspoon salt

½ teaspoon ground black pepper

1/3 teaspoon peppercorn

½ teaspoon ground black pepper

1/3 teaspoon dried thyme

Step 2:

1 tablespoon vegetable oil

Optional: Apricot sauce

1 large apricot

2 tablespoons water

2 teaspoons sugar

Directions

1) Peel, core, and mash the apricot—mash with two tablespoons of water.
2) After the breasts are cleaned, rub them with all of the ingredients.
3) Cover in the refrigerator for about two hours. Rinse off the spices and place them in a Ziploc baggie—removing the air—seal it.
4) Add the water to the seven-cup marker in the Instant Pot. Turn the power to keep warm. Put the baggie in the bath for about 35 to 40 minutes.
5) Take the baggie from the Instant Pot and pat the duck dry with a couple of paper towels.
6) Place one tablespoon of oil in a non-stick pan and sear both sides of the duck. Flip and cook the other side 20 seconds.
7) Slice and serve with the below Apricot Sauce.
8) *Apricot Sauce*: Blend the mashed apricot, 2 tablespoons, of water and the sugar. Using a small pot, bring the ingredients to a boil on high and simmer on low for approximately five minutes.

Yields: 2 servings

Duck and Veggies

Ingredients

1 Medium-sized duck

2 carrots

1 cucumber

2 cups water

2 tablespoons wine1 tablespoon cooking wine

2 teaspoons salt

1 small piece of ginger cut into pieces

Directions

- Cut the cucumber and carrots into pieces.
- Place each of the ingredients into the IP and press the meat-stew button.
- That is it!

Yields: 8 servings

Creamy Sweet Potato Puree

Ingredients

1 ½ cups pork or bone broth (under soups)

2 pounds sweet potatoes

½ teaspoon sea salt

Directions

1) Peel and cut the potatoes into one-inch bites.

2) Pour the bone broth and potatoes into the IP.

3) Set the pressure cook setting to ten minutes.

4) After it reaches the low- boil, cover, and let them steam fifteen minutes.

5) Whip the broth, potatoes, and salt for thirty seconds or until the puree is silky using a food processor.

Yields: Serves 6

Glazed Carrots

Ingredients

2 teaspoons butter

1/2cup water

1 pound carrots

1 teaspoon honey

1/3 cup brown sugar

Directions

1) Pour the water to the Instant Pot, putting the carrots in the bottom.

2) Place the remainder of the ingredients on top of the carrots.

3) Use the manual setting for five minutes.

It is ready to serve.

Instant Pot Gravy

This is also gluten-free and grain-free. It can also be made ahead of time to avoid the rushing about before your Christmas or Thanksgiving dinner.

Ingredients

1 whole raw chicken

2 pieces uncooked bacon

1 cup bone broth (recipe in the lunch section - Chapter 2)

2 large onions

1 ounce dried mushrooms

5 ounces fresh mushrooms

¼ cup duck fat, butter, or bacon fat (animal fat)

½ teaspoon black or white pepper (plus ¼ teaspoon)

1 teaspoon each:

- Onion powder
- Thyme
- Sage

- Sea salt (plus ¼ teaspoon)

Directions

1) Peel and cut the onions in halves.
2) Add the broth, onions, dried and fresh mushrooms, animal fat, bacon, thyme, sage, and ½ teaspoon of salt. Put the chicken on top, sprinkling the remainder of the pepper and salt.
3) Place the lid on the Instant Pot, seal, making sure the seals are tight.
4) Select the poultry setting for 15 minutes. Use the natural release function for about 15 minutes; then QR for the remainder of the steam pressure.
5) Remove the lid and let it cool until you can handle it without being burned. Transfer it to a dish and remove its skin. Set it to the side. You can use the meat for chicken salad, a casserole or some soup.
6) Transfer the solid foods from the IP, and add three cups of the liquid to a blender.
7) Combine the chicken skin, onion powder, black pepper, and sea salt to the liquid. Puree using medium-high for about fifty to sixty seconds, or until smooth.

Note: If you need to reheat the gravy; simply pour it into a saucepan and add some of the leftover juices from the IP if it is too thick.

Yields: 6 ½ cups

IP Green Beans

Ingredients

½ tablespoon butter

¼ cup bacon bits

A pinch of salt and pepper

1 pound green beans

Directions

1) Pour one cup of water in the Instant Pot.
2) Place the steamer rack in the pot.
3) Pour the beans and bacon in the pot and cook three minutes.
4) Serve with the butter and additional pieces of bacon bits.

Note: If you like softer green beans; you should continue to cook them for an additional five minutes or so until you have them to the desired consistency.

Instant Pot Cranberry Sauce

This is one of those recipes that can be used for holidays, as a glaze for meats, as a spread, a dessert topping, or what about with a smoothie or yogurt?

Ingredients

2 ½ teaspoons orange zest

¼ cup orange juice 12-ounces cranberries (divided)

Optional:

Pinch of salt

2 Tbsp. honey or maple syrup

½ to 1 cup white sugar

Directions

1) Prepare the cranberries by removing the stems and rinsing them under running cold water. Throw away any of the shriveled or discolored berries.
2) Combine the orange juice and maple syrup in the IP.
3) Toss in approximately 10-ounces of the cranberries and orange zest.
4) Close the lid and cook for one minute (+) seven using the natural release.

5) Use caution when you open the lid and do not get burned by the steam.
6) *For the Sauce*: Turn the IP to medium heat and blend in the berries with the white sugar.
7) You can use a bit of salt and a bit little more sugar for additional flavor for the berries.

Delicious IP Pumpkin Pie

Ingredients for the Crust

2 Tbsp. unsalted melted butter

20 crushed ginger snaps

Ingredients for the Filling

1 cup pumpkin puree

1 egg

¼ cup each: white and brown sugar

1 tsp. cinnamon

½ cup half-and-half

¼ tsp. each:

- Ginger
- Salt
- Cloves

- Nutmeg
- Allspice

Directions

1) Prepare a seven-inch spring-form pan. Sit the pan on a paper towel, and a layer of aluminum foil, which is used to wrap the pan before you place it into the Instant Pot.
2) You will also need to make a sling using some foil to wrap around the pan to remove it from the pot when the pie is done.
3) Use a rolling pin or a food processor to crush the cookies. Stir in the butter and continue stirring.
4) Place the mixture into the spring-form pan—pressing evenly on the bottom and up the sides. Let it rest for about 15 minutes in the freezer.
5) Clean the processor bowl; combine the filling ingredients and blend for about twenty seconds. You can also mix it in a large mixing bowl. Pour the pie mix into the crust. Place a piece of foil over the pie.
6) Pour one cup of water to the IP, put the trivet in the pot, and lower the pan using a foil sling (made from the aluminum foil strips).

7) Lock the lid and manually set the pot for 35 minutes on the high-pressure setting making sure the lid is sealed correctly.
8) Allow the unit to perform a natural release. Use the foil sling to remove the pie and place it in the refrigerator until it is thoroughly cooled.
9) Serve with some whipped cream for an additional treat!

New Year's Day: Black-eyed Peas and Ham

Ingredients

6 ½ cups stock (vegetable, ham, or chicken plus 2 tablespoons 'Better Than Bullion Chicken Base')

1 pound dried black-eyed peas (rinsed)

5 ounces diced ham

Instructions

1) No need to presoak the beans; rinse them.
2) Toss all of the ingredients into the Instant Pot, close the lid, and lock it.
3) Use high-pressure setting it manually for thirty minutes. Let it release naturally.

Note: If you like firmer peas; reduce the time by a few minutes at a time.

Yields: 10 servings

Chapter 5

Easter Recipes

Ingredients

1 Lb. rack of lamb

2 carrots

1 Lb. baby potatoes

1 large onion

2 medium size tomatoes

2 stalks of celery

3 to 4 large garlic cloves

2 cups chicken stock

2 teaspoons each:

- Cumin powder
- Paprika

2 Tbsp. of ketchup

A splash of beer (if handy)

3 Tbsp. red wine or sherry

A pinch of oregano leaves and rosemary

Directions

1) Wash all of the vegetables. Cut the carrots and potatoes into one-inch cubes. Dice the garlic, onion, and tomatoes. Cut the lamb into two halves.

2) Place everything into the Instant Pot and blend well.

3) Close the lid and set the stew/meat function for 30 minutes.

4) Allow the lamb to perform the natural release.

5) Serve over multigrain rice or regular rice.

Yields: 6 to 8 servings

Lamb Shanks with Figs and Ginger

This is excellent if you are searching for a Paleo diet recipe.

Ingredients

4 (12-ounce) lamb shanks

2 Tbsp. coconut oil

1 large sliced onion

2 to 3 finely minced garlic cloves

2 tsp. fish sauce

2 Tbsp. each:

- fresh minced ginger
- apple cider vinegar
- coconut aminos

10 dried figs

1 ½ C. bone broth (*See Chapter 2 – Lunch*)

Directions

1) Slice the onion 'pole to pole.' Remove the stems and cut the figs lengthwise.
2) Set the Instant Pot on the sauté function; add one tablespoon of the coconut oil to the pot.
3) Put two of the shanks into the IP, turning occasionally, and brown all sides. Place in a bowl or plate, and repeat with the remainder of the oil and two shanks and set to the side. Set the juices to the side for step 6.
4) Combine the ginger and onion into the empty pot for about three minutes (stirring frequently).
5) Blend in the garlic, fish sauce, coconut aminos, and vinegar; stirring in the figs and broth while scraping the brown bits from the bottom of the IP.
6) Return the reserved juices and lamb shank making sure the meat is covered with liquid; lock the lid.
7) Set the Instant Pot to the high-pressure setting for one hour. Turn off the machine and use the natural release function. Open the cooker and place the shanks in a serving dish.
8) Skim away the surface fat and throw it away.
9) Pour the sauce over the shanks and serve with some rice.

Yields: 4 servings

Osso Bucco

Ingredients

4 lamb or veal shanks

¼ cup flour

½ teaspoon each:

- Onion powder
- Salt
- Garlic powder
- Black pepper

1 teaspoon each of rosemary and thyme

1 Tablespoon butter

¼ cup olive oil

2 stalks celery

2 medium carrots

2 crushed garlic cloves

1 medium/large chopped onion

1 to 2 cups chicken broth (depending on the pot size)

2 Lbs. washed red potatoes

2 Tablespoons butter

Directions

1) Rinse the shanks and dry in between two paper towels.
2) Chop the celery and carrots into big chunks.
3) Combine the seasonings in a large bowl—whisking everything together.
4) Roll the meat in the flour mixture and set to the side on a plate. Reserve the mixture to use later (step #5).
5) Using a large pan, add the oil—heat—and add the shanks browning each side. Set them to the side.
6) Add the flour to the oil to process a rue. Also, add the broth and loosen the rue to make the sauce.
7) Pour half of the sauce into the IP, placing the shanks in the sauce (placed upright). Put the veggies between the gaps. Pour the rest of the sauce over the mixture and meat.
8) Seal the cooker for 90 minutes.
9) Boil the potatoes with the skins on; mash, and add the butter.
10) Place a shank over the potato bed and enjoy the lovely meal.

Yields: 4 servings

Chocolate Cake for Easter

Ingredients

¼ cup mashed avocado

1 green plantain

½ of a ripe banana

2 Tbsp. honey

2 Tbsp. melted coconut oil

½ Tsp. apple cider vinegar

5 Tbsp. carob powder

¾ Tsp. baking soda

1 cup water

⅛ Tsp. cream of tartar

Optional Garnishes: Fruit, coconut flakes, or coconut cream

Note: You will need more coconut oil for greasing the pans.

Directions

1) Using a food processor, combine the avocado, banana, plantain, honey, coconut oil, carob, cream of tartar, and baking soda. Combine the ingredients, blending until smooth.
2) Prepare three mini fluted pans or ramekins by greasing them with a bit of coconut oil. Fill the pans ¾ full.
3) Add the steaming rack to the pot and pour the cup of water into the IP.

4) Put the pans on the rack. Close and lock the top. Use high pressure for 18 minutes.
5) When the time is finished, use the quick release, and remove the pans.

Garnish and enjoy with your family and friends!

Chapter 6

Saint Patrick's Day Recipes

Corned Beef and Cabbage Luncheon/Dinner

This traditional dish takes less than half of the time as usual when preparing it in your Instant Pot cooker. You won't be able to wait for dinner!

Ingredients

3 whole black peppercorns

4 cups of water

3 to 4 pounds corned beef brisket

3 garlic cloves (smashed and peeled)

1 small onion (quartered)

2 bay leaves

½ teaspoon whole allspice berries

1 teaspoon dried thyme

5 medium carrots

1 ½ pounds red potato

1 head of cabbage (wedges)

Directions

1) Combine the water, corned beef, garlic cloves, onion quarters, peppercorns, thyme, and allspice into the pot.

2) Lock the lid and use the manual button to set the timer for ninety minutes.

3) After the brisket cycle is complete; turn off the cooker and let it release naturally (usually ten additional minutes); Quick release the remainder pressure.

4) Remove the meat out of the pot and put it in a covered dish. Use a piece of heavy-duty aluminum foil (tightly cover it) for a fifteen minute rest time.

5) For the time being; add the cabbage, potatoes, and carrots to the pot of liquids.

6) Switch the Instant Pot to the manual setting and adjust the time for ten minutes.

7) Use the quick release to open the pot.

8) Serve the vegetables with the corned beef.

Tip: You can use some of the liquid if needed to moisten the corned beef.

Yields: Serves 6

Cabbage and Cream

Ingredients

1 cup bacon or lardon (pork fat strips)

2 cups bone broth (*see Chapter 2*)

1 onion

1 medium head (around 2 pounds) Savoy cabbage

½ can coconut milk (scant 1 cup or 200 ml)

¼ teaspoon mace or nutmeg

1 bay leaf

2 tablespoons parsley flakes

Sea salt (to taste)

Directions

1) Dice the bacon and chop the onion. Finely chop the cabbage.
2) Cut out a parchment round to use in the inner pot. Let the Instant Pot warm up using the sauté function. When you see the 'hot' light; add the onions and bacon and cook until each are lightly browned.
3) Pour in the bone broth, scraping to get the stuck brown bits (they are good).
4) Toss in the bay leaf and cabbage.
5) Use the parchment paper on the top and close the lid, sealing the valve.
6) Use the manual setting for four minutes.

7) After the beep, press the keep warm-cancel button and release the pressure. Remove the parchment round.
8) Use the sauté function to bring the juices to a boil, adding the nutmeg or mace with the milk.
9) Simmer for about five minutes; turn off the IP, and stir. Enjoy!

Yields: 4 to 6 servings

Chapter 7

4th of July Recipes

New York Dirty Hot Dogs

Ingredients

1 quart of water

6 hotdogs (not skinless)

6 hot dog buns

1 Tbsp. white or red vinegar

⅛ Tsp. whole nutmeg (freshly grated)

½ tsp. cumin

Directions

1) Pour the water, vinegar, nutmeg, and cumin into the Instant Pot.
2) Add the hot dogs and lock the lid, making sure you close the pressure valve.
3) Cook at the lowest pressure setting for three minutes, using the natural release feature.
4) Serve on the buns and have a great lunch and enjoy the holiday.

Yields: 3 servings

IP Marinated Steak

Ingredients

2 Lbs. flank steak

2 Tbsp. onion soup mix

½ C. olive oil

1 Tbsp. Worcestershire sauce

¼ C. apple cider vinegar

Directions

1) Set the Instant Pot to the sauté function and add the olive oil along with the steak.
2) Sauté each side of the steak until browned.
3) Pour in the Worcestershire sauce, vinegar, and soup mix.
4) Lock the lid and seal the steam nozzle.
5) Place the Instant Pot on the meat/stew setting or set it manually for 35 minutes.
6) Naturally release the pressure for five minutes, and QR the rest of the pressure.

Serve and enjoy your steak.

Yields: 4 servings

Bring On the Chicken

Honey Barbecue Wings

Ingredients

½ cup honey

½ cup water

2 pounds chicken wings: thawed or frozen

2 tablespoons Worcestershire sauce

1 cup BBQ sauce (favorite)

½ cup brown sugar

1 tablespoon minced fresh garlic

Optional: ½ teaspoon cayenne pepper/crushed

Directions

1) Combine all of the ingredients into the Instant Pot. Seal and set the valve.
2) *Note*: Frozen wings = Twelve minutes

   Thawed wings = Ten minutes
3) Quick release the valve and place the chicken on a foil-lined pan.
4) Baste with more BBQ sauce.
5) Broil five minutes on high until the chicken is caramelized.
6) Flip them over, baste, and broil for two additional minutes.

Oven Style Barbecue Baby-Back Ribs

Ingredients

1 Rack of ribs (your choice)

4 tablespoons (your favorite) BBQ sauce

Directions Part One:

1) Cut the membrane away from each of the ribs.
2) Place one cup of cold water with a pinch of salt in the pot, and put the trivet into the IP.
3) Put the ribs on top of the trivet. Set the ribs to cook for 15 to 25 minutes using high pressure.
4) Wait for the full natural release and use caution when you open the lid.
5) *Note the Times*: Fall off the bone: 25 minutes or Tender with a bit of chew: 15 minutes

Directions Part Two:

1) Preset the oven to 450 °F while the ribs are cooking in the Instant Pot.
2) Apply the BBQ sauce on each side of the meat and sit them on the baking tray for ten to fifteen minutes.

Enjoy the evening!

Cola Chicken Wings

Ingredients

1 stalk green onion 1 ½ pounds chicken wings

4 crushed garlic cloves

1 tablespoon each:

- Sliced ginger
- Peanut oil
- Dark soy sauce

Chinese rice wine 200 ml (7 ounces)

Regular Coca Cola

2 Tbsp. Light soy sauce

Directions

1) Cut the onion into two-inch long sections.
2) Heat up the IP using the sauté function. It is ready when the 'hot' indicator is on.
3) Pour the oil into the pot, and add the onions, ginger, and garlic.
4) Add the wings to the IP and stir the mixture for about one to two minutes.
5) When the chicken begins to brown, pour in the cola. Use a wooden spoon to deglaze the pot.
6) Pour in the dark soy sauce, Chinese rice wine, and light soy sauce.

7) Close the lid and set the pot on high pressure for five minutes.
8) Turn the IP off after the time is completed using a full natural release— which will take about ten minutes.
9) Open the lid and perform a taste test to see if you need more salt. The chicken should not taste like the cola at this point. You can serve with rice or other dishes.

Yields: 2 to 4 servings

Pina Colada Chicken

Ingredients

2 pounds chicken thighs

½ cup full-fat coconut cream

1 cup frozen or fresh pineapple chunks

⅛ teaspoon of salt

2 tablespoons coconut Aminos

1 teaspoon cinnamon

Garnish: ½ cup green onion

Directions

1) Prepare the thighs by cutting each piece into one-inch chunks.
2) Put all of the ingredients in the Instant Pot, except for the onions.

3) Close the top and select the poultry function which automatically sets high pressure for fifteen minutes.
4) When the cycle is completed; turn the IP off and let the pressure release naturally in ten minutes.
5) Open the lid and take the chicken out of the pot; stir the ingredients.
6) If you decide on a thicker sauce; add one teaspoon of arrowroot starch mixed with one tablespoon of water and stir it in the pot. Continue cooking until it is thick to your liking.
7) Turn the pot off and enjoy the chicken with an onion garnish.

Note: Coconut Aminos is 100% organic with 17 naturally occurring amino acids. It is also an excellent choice for a Vegan diet plan.

Sides for the Picnic

Instant Pot Potato Salad

Ingredients

2 to 2 ½ Lbs. potatoes

4 large eggs

1 ½ cups of water

For the Dressing:

2 tablespoons fresh parsley

1 Tbsp. yellow mustard

¾ cup olive oil or light mayonnaise

1 minced dill pickle spear

¼ cup scallions (the white sections) or onions

1 chopped rib of celery

1 teaspoon of each of seasoned salt & sea salt

The Garnish: ½ to 1 tsp. paprika

Optional: 1 Tbsp. fresh dill weed

Directions

1) Soak the raw potatoes in water for a minimum of thirty minutes.
2) Put the eggs and potatoes into the steamer/trivet basket with the water.
3) Close the pressure valve and lock the lid. Cook four minutes using high pressure.
4) In the meantime, blend the dressing ingredients, and set them aside for the time being.
5) After the time is complete; perform the quick release.
6) Place the eggs in some cold water for a few minutes—then peel.
7) Dice or mince the eggs and mix with the potatoes.
8) Pour in the dressing mixture and combine thoroughly.

9) Cover the dish—chilling thoroughly before serving.

Yummy IP Macaroni and Cheese

Ingredients

4 cups cold water 1 package (16 ounces) elbow macaroni

4 Tbsp. unsalted butter

2 large eggs

14 ounces sharp cheddar cheese

1 tsp. hot sauce

12 ounces evaporated milk

1 tsp. ground mustard

Directions

1) Use the pressure cooking function and pour the macaroni in the Instant Pot with a pinch of salt along with the water.
2) Shut the lid and let the pressure cook it for approximately four minutes.
3) Use the quick release to open the IP. (It's normal to foam a little, just wipe it away with a paper towel.)
4) For the time being, mix the eggs, milk, hot sauce, and ground mustard in a medium dish.
5) Leave the Instant Pot on the warming function.

6) Add the butter to the macaroni and mix until the butter melts.

7) Steadily, blend in the cheese; while continuing to stir the mixture in the pot until thoroughly melted.

Yields: Serves 4 to 6 people

Patriotic Red, White, and Blue Cheesecake Singles

Ingredients

1 (16-ounces) package cream cheese

25 vanilla or cinnamon graham crackers

½ cup sugar

Optional: 1 Vanilla bean caviar scraped

½ teaspoon vanilla extract

Optional: 1 teaspoon all-purpose flour

½ teaspoon each of lemon and orange peel (grated)

3 tablespoons heavy whipping cream

3 eggs at room temperature

Middle layer: Berry Compote (see recipe below)

Garnishes:

- Blueberries
- Strawberries
- Whipped Cream

12 (4-ounce) mason jars

Directions for the Crust and Filling

1) Crush the wafers and place them into the jars. You will add approximately two tablespoons.

2) Blend the sugar, cream cheese, flour, vanilla bean extract, and vanilla bean caviar until the mixture is smooth. Combine the grated peels and cream.
3) Blend in the eggs, until just combined.
4) Add two tablespoons of the cheesecake mix to the jars. Add a tablespoon of compote to each jar, and finally, two more tablespoons of the cheese mix to the jar.

Cook:

1) Add 1 ½ cups of water to the Instant Pot and put the trivet in the bottom.
2) Place the six jars into the trivet; placing a second trivet in over the jars. Add the last jars to the pot, adding a layer of foil–loosely over the top.
3) Lock and close the lid and pressure valve, cooking for four minutes on the high- pressure cycle. Permit the ten-minute natural release.
4) Let them cool a minimum of five hours or overnight in the refrigerator.
5) Garnish with some blueberries, strawberries, and whipped cream.

Enjoy the 4th of July celebration!

Yields: 12 servings

Instant Pot Fresh Berry Compote

You can use any berries of your choice.

Ingredients

1 Lb. Strawberries

1 Lb. Blueberries

2 tsp. lemon or orange juice

¼ C. sugar

Optional:

- Ground Cinnamon
- Whole Nutmeg
- Vanilla Bean

Directions

1) Wash, trim, and cut the strawberries in half. Wash the blueberries. Add the fruit to the IP. Drizzle with sugar and let stand for twenty minutes.
2) Add the preferred juice. Lock the lid and close the pressure valve.
3) Cook on the high-pressure setting for one minute.
4) When the time is complete; use the natural pressure release for fifteen minutes.

The compote will thicken during the cooling process.

Yields: 4 cups

Index

Chapter 1: Breakfast Recipes

Chapter 2: Lunch Recipes

Broth—Soups—& Stews

Sandwiches

Chapter 7: Fourth of July

- New York Dirty Hot Dogs
- IP Marinated Steak

Bring On the Chicken

- Honey Barbecue Wings
- Oven Style Barbecue Baby-Back Ribs
- Cola Chicken Wings
- Pina Colada Chicken

Sides for the Picnic

- Instant Pot Potato Salad
- Yummy IP Macaroni and Cheese

Desserts

- Patriotic Red, White, and Blue Cheesecake Singles
- Instant Pot Fresh Berry Compote for the Cheesecake

PART IV

Chapter 1: Keto Basics

Benefits of Increased Metabolism

One of the best ways to learn the meaning of a scientific term is to break it down to its roots. When we break down ketogenic, we see it is comprised of two words: keto and genic. Ketones are fat-based molecules that the body breaks down when it is using fat as its energy source. When used as a suffix, "genic" means "causing, forming, or producing." So, we put these terms together, and we have "ketogenic," or simply put, "causing fat burn." Ergo, the theory behind ketogenic dieting is: when a person reduces the amount of sugar and carbohydrates they consume, the body will begin to breakdown fat it already has in stores all over the body. When your body is cashing in on these stores, it is in a ketogenic state, or "ketosis." When your body consumes food, it naturally seeks carbohydrates for the purpose of breaking them down and using them as fuel. Adversely, a ketogenic cleanse trains your body to use fats for energy instead. This is achieved by lowering the amount of ingested carbohydrates and increasing the amount of ingested fats, which in turn boosts your metabolism.

Only recently has a low carb- high-fat diet plan emerged into the public eye. It is a sharp contrast to the traditional dieting style that emphasizes calorie counting. For many years it was overlooked that crash diets neglect the most important aspect of dieting: food is fuel. A diet is not meant to be treated as a once a year go to method in order to shed holiday weight in January. Rather, a diet is a lifestyle; it is a consistent pattern of how individual fuels their body. A ten day ketogenic cleanse is the perfect way to begin forming healthy eating habits that over time become second nature. If you are tired of losing weight just to gain it all back, never fear. We firmly believe that you can accomplish anything you put your mind to, including living a healthy life! You, like hundreds of others, can successfully accomplish a ketogenic cleanse and change the way you see health, fitness, and life along the way. So let's hit the books and get that metabolism working!

Benefits of Cleansing

In addition to increased metabolism and fat loss, ketogenic cleansing allows your body naturally rid itself of harmful toxins and wasteful substances. In today's modern world, food is overrun and polluted by genetically modified hormones, artificial flavors and coloring, and copious amounts of unnecessary sugars. Ketogenic cleansing eliminates bread, grains, and many other foods that are most affected by today's modern industrialization. Due to the high amount of naturally occurring foods used in a ketogenic cleanse, the body is able to obtain many vitamins and minerals that are not prevalent in a high carb diet. When the body is consuming sufficient amounts of necessary vitamins and minerals, it is able to heal itself and maintain a healthy immune system. Cleansing your body is one of the best ways to achieve, and maintain pristine health.

Chapter 2: Meal Plan Madness

One of the best ways to stay motivated, when dieting, is to find a meal plan that is easy to follow and easy on the budget. Ketogenic meals are designed to be filling while keeping within the perimeters of low-carb, high-fat guidelines. Ideally, you want to aim for 70% fats, 25% protein, and 5% carbohydrates in your diet. As long as the materials you use to build your meals are low in carbs and high in fats, feel free to experiment and find what is right for you. Each and every one of us is different, and that's okay. After all, this meal plan is for YOU!

Below is a ten-day meal plan, designed with a busy schedule in mind, which will not break the bank! All of these meals can be prepared in 30 minutes or less, and many of them are much quicker than that! There is also a list of ingredients for each meal located in the recipe chapter so you can go to the grocery store knowing exactly what you need!

	Breakfast	**Lunch**	**Dinner**
Day 1	**California Chicken Omelet** • Fat: 32 grams • 10 minutes to prepare • Protein: 25 grams • 10 minutes of cooking • Net carbs: 4	**Cobb Salad** • Fat: 48 grams • 10 minutes to prepare • Protein: 43 grams • 0 minutes of cooking • Net carbs: 3	**Chicken Peanut Pad Thai** • Fat: 12 grams • 15 minutes to prepare • Protein: 30 grams • 15 minutes

	grams	grams	of cooking • Net carbs: 2 g
Day 2	**Easy Blender Pancakes** • Fat: 29 grams • 5 minutes to prepare • Protein: 41 grams • 10 minutes of cooking • Net carbs: 4 grams	**Sardine Stuffed Avocados** • Fat: 29 grams • 10 minutes to prepare • Protein: 27 grams • 0 minutes of cooking • Net Carbs: 5 grams	**Chipotle Fish Tacos** • Fat: 20 grams • 5 minutes to prepare • Protein: 24 grams • 15 minutes of cooking • Net carbs: 5 grams
Day 3	**Steak and Eggs** • Fat: 36 grams • 10 minutes to prepare • Protein: 47 grams • 5 minutes of cooking • Net carbs: 3	**Low-Carb Smoothie Bowl** • Fat 35 grams • 5 minutes to prepare • Protein: 20 grams • 0 minutes of cooking	**Avocado Lime Salmon** • Fat: 27 grams • 20 minutes to prepare • Protein: 37 grams • 10 minutes

	grams	• Net carbs: 5 grams	of cooking • Net carbs: 5 grams
KEEP IT UP!!!	During the course of your plan, especially around days 3 and 4, you may begin to feel like you don't have it in you. You may have thoughts telling you that you cannot last for ten days on this type pf cleanse. Do not allow feelings of discouragement bother you because, guess what? We all feel that way sometimes! A ketogenic diet causes your body to process energy like it never has before. Keep pressing on! Your body will thank you and so will you!		
Day 4	**Low-Carb Smoothie Bowl** • Fat: 35 grams • 5 minutes to prepare • Protein: 35 grams • 0 minutes of cooking • Net carbs: 4 grams	**Pesto Chicken Salad** • Fat: 27 grams • 5 minutes to prepare • Protein: 27 grams • 10 minutes of cooking • Net carbs: 3 g	**Siracha Lime Flank Steak** • Fat: 32 grams • 5 minutes to prepare • Protein: 48 grams • 10 minutes of cooking • Net Carbs: 5 g
Day 5	**Feta and Pesto Omelet**	**Roasted Brussel Sprouts**	**Low carb Sesame**

	• Fat: 46 grams • 5 minutes of preparation • Protein: 30 grams • 5 minutes of cooking • Net carbs: 2.5 grams	• Fat: 21 grams • 5 minutes to prepare • Protein: 21 grams • 30 minutes of cooking • Net carbs: 4 grams	**Chicken** • Fat: 36 grams • 15 minutes to prepare • Protein: 41 grams • 15 minutes of cooking • Net carbs: 4 grams
Day 6	**Raspberry Cream Crepes** • Fat: 40 grams • 5 minutes of preparation • Net carbs: 8 grams • 15 minutes of cooking • Protein 15 grams	**Shakshuka** • Fat: 34 grams • Protein 35 grams • Net carbs: 4 grams • 10 minutes of preparation • 10 minutes of cooking	**Sausage in a Pan** • Fat: 38 grams • 10 minutes of preparation • Protein: 30 grams • 25 minutes of cooking • Net Carbs: 4

			grams
Day 7	**Green Monster Smoothie** • Fat: 25 grams • 5 minutes of preparation • Protein: 30 grams • 0 minutes of cooking • Net Carbs: 3 grams	**Tuna Tartare** • Fat: 24 grams • 15 minutes of preparation • Protein: 56 grams • 0 minutes of cooking • Net Carbs: 4 grams	**Pesto Chicken Salad** • Fat: 27 grams • 5 minutes of preparation • Protein: 27 grams • 10 minutes of cooking • Net carbs: 3 grams
ALMOST THERE!!	By now, you can be certain you are seeing physical results such as reduced body fat and more energy! You are doing a fantastic job and you only have three days left! Keep up the good work, you owe it to yourself.		
Day 8	**Shakshuka** • Fat: 34 grams • 10 minutes of preparation	**Grilled Halloumi Salad** • Fat: 47 grams	**Keto Quarter Pounder** • Fat: 34 grams

	• Protein 35 grams • 10 minutes of cooking • Net carbs: 4 grams	• 15 minutes of preparation • Protein: 21 grams • 0 minutes of cooking • Net carbs: 2 grams	• 10 minutes of preparation • Protein: 25 grams • 8 minutes of cooking • Net carbs: 4 grams
Day 9	**Easy Blender Pancakes** • Fat: 29 grams • 5 minutes of preparation • Protein: 41 grams • 10 minutes of cooking • Net carbs: 4 grams	**Broccoli Bacon Salad** • Fat: 31 grams • 15 minutes of preparation • Protein: 10 grams • 6 minutes of cooking • Net carbs: 5 grams	**Sardine Stuffed Avocados** • Fat: 29 grams • 10 minutes to prepare • Protein: 27 grams • 0 minutes to cook • Net Carbs: 5 grams
Day 10	**California Chicken Omelet**	**Shrimp Scampi** • Fat: 21	**Tuna Tartare**

	• Fat 32 grams • 10 minutes to prepare • Protein 25 grams • 10 minutes of cooking • Net carb: 3 grams	grams • 5 minutes to prepare • Protein: 21 grams • 30 minutes of cooking • Net carbs: 4 grams	• Fat: 36 grams • 15 minutes to prepare • Protein: 41 grams • 15 minutes of cooking • Net carbs: 4 grams
YOU DID IT!!	Congratulations! You have successfully completed a 10 day ketogenic cleanse. By now your body has adjusted to its new source of energy, expelled dozens of harmful toxins, and replenished itself with many vitamins and minerals it may have been lacking. Way to go on a job well done!		

Chapter 3: Breakfast Is For Champions

Breakfast is by far the most important meal of the day for one reason: it set the tone for the rest of your day. In order to hit the ground running, it is vital that one starts each day with foods that fuel an energetic and productive day. This chapter contains ten ketogenic breakfast ides that will have you burning fat and conquering your day like you never imagined.

1. California Chicken Omelet

- This recipe requires 10 minutes of preparation, 10 minutes of cooking time and serves 1
- Net carbs: 4 grams
- Protein: 25 grams
- Fat : 32 grams

What you will need:

- Mayo (1 tablespoon)
- Mustard (1 teaspoon)
- Campari tomato
- Eggs (2 large beaten)
- Avocado (one fourth, sliced)
- Bacon (2 slices cooked and chopped)
- Deli chicken (1 ounce)

What to do:

1. Place a skillet on the stove over a burner set to a medium heat and let it warm before adding in the eggs and seasoning as needed.
2. Once eggs are cooked about halfway through, add bacon, chicken, avocado, tomato, mayo, and mustard on one side of the eggs.
3. Fold the omelet onto its self, cover and cook for 5 additional minutes.

4. Once eggs are fully cooked and all ingredients are warm, through the center, your omelet is ready.
5. Bon apatite!

2. Steak and Eggs with Avocado

- This recipe requires 10 minutes of preparation, 5 minutes of cooking time and serves 1
- Net Carbs: 3 grams
- Protein: 44 grams
- Fat: 36 grams

What you will need:

- Salt and pepper
- Avocado (one fourth, sliced)
- Sirloin steak (4 ounce)
- Eggs (3 large)
- Butter (1 tablespoon)

What to do:

1. Melt the tablespoon of butter in a pan and fry all 3 eggs to desired doneness. Season the eggs with salt and pepper.
2. In a different pan, cook the sirloin steak to your preferred taste and slice it into thin strips. Season the steak with salt and pepper.
3. Sever your prepared steak and eggs with slices of avocado.
4. Enjoy!

3. Pancakes an a Blender

- This recipe requires 5 minutes of preparation, 10 minutes of cooking time and serves 1
- Net Carbs: 4 grams
- Protein: 41 grams
- Fat: 29 grams

What you will need:

- Whey protein powder (1 scoop)
- Eggs (2 large)
- Cream cheese (2 ounces)
- Just a pinch of cinnamon and a pinch of salt

What to do:

1. Combine cream cheese, eggs, protein powder, cinnamon, and salt into a blender. Blend for 10 seconds and let stand.
2. While letting batter stand, warm a skillet over medium heat.
3. Pour about ¼ of the batter onto warmed skillet and let cook. When bubbles begin to emerge on the surface, flip the pancake.
4. Once flipped, cook for 15 seconds. Repeat until remainder of the batter is used up.
5. Top with butter and/ or sugar- free maple syrup and you are all set!
6. Chow time!

4. Low Carb Smoothe Bowl

- Net Carbs: 4 grams
- Protein: 35 grams
- Fat: 35 grams
- Takes 5 minutes to prepare and serves 1.

What you will need:

- Spinach (1 cup)
- Almond milk (half a cup)
- Coconut oil (1 tablespoon)
- Low carb protein powder (1 scoop)
- Ice cubes (2 cubes)
- Whipping cream (2 T)
- Optional toppings can include: raspberries, walnuts, shredded coconut, or chia seeds

What to do:

1. Place spinach in blender. Add almond milk, cream, coconut oil, and ice. Blend until thoroughly and evenly combined.
2. Pour into bowl.
3. Top with toppings or stir lightly into smoothie.
4. Treat yourself!

5. Feta and Pesto Omelet

- This recipe requires 5 minutes of preparation, 5 minutes of cooking time and serves 1
- Net Carbs: 2.5 grams
- Protein: 30 grams
- Fat: 46 grams

What you will need:

- Butter (1 tablespoon)
- Eggs (3 large)
- Heavy cream (1 tablespoon)
- Feta cheese (1 ounce)
- Basil pesto (1 teaspoon)
- Tomatoes (optional)

What to do:

1. Heat pan and melt butter.
2. Beat eggs together with heavy whipping cream (will give eggs a fluffy consistency once cooked).
3. Pour eggs in pan and cook until almost done, add feta and pesto to on half of eggs.
4. Fold omelet and cook for an additional 4-5 minutes.
5. Top with feta and tomatoes, and eat up!

6. Crepes with Cream and Raspberries

- This recipe requires 5 minutes of preparation, 15 minutes of cooking time and serves 2
- Net Carbs: 8 grams
- Protein: 15 grams
- Fat: 40 grams

What you will need:

- Raspberries (3 ounces, fresh or frozen)
- Whole Milk Ricotta (half a cup and 2 tablespoons)
- Erythritol (2 tablespoons)
- Eggs (2 large)
- Cream Cheese (2 ounces)
- Pinch of salt
- Dash of Cinnamon
- Whipped cream and sugar- free maple syrup to go on top

What to do:

1. In a blender, blend cream cheese, eggs, erythritol, salt, and cinnamon for about 20 seconds, or until there are no lumps of cream cheese.
2. Place a pan on a burner turned to a medium heat before coating in cooking spray. Add 20 percent of your batter to the pan in a thin layer. Cook crepe until the underside becomes slightly

darkened. Carefully flip the crepe and let the reverse side cook for about 15 seconds.

3. Repeat step 3 until all batter is used.
4. Without stacking the crepes, allow them to cool for a few minutes.
5. After the crepes have cool, place about 2 tablespoons of ricotta cheese in the center of each crepe.
6. Throw in a couple of raspberries and fold the side to the middle.
7. Top those off with some whipped cream and sugar- free maple syrup and…
8. Viola! You're a true chef! Indulge in your creation!

7. Green Monster Smoothie

- This recipe requires 10 minutes of preparation, 0 minutes of cooking time and serves 1
- Net Carbs: 4 grams
- Protein: 30 grams
- Fat: 25 grams

What you will need:

- Almond milk (one and a half cups)
- Spinach (one eighth of a cup)
- Cucumber (fourth of a cup)
- Celery (fourth of a cup)
- Avocado (fourth of a cup)
- Coconut oil (1 tablespoon)
- Stevia (liquid, 10 drops)
- Whey Protein Powder (1 scoop)

What to do:

1. In a blender, blend almond milk and spinach for a few pulses.
2. Add remaining ingredients and blend until thoroughly combined.

- Add optional matcha powder, if desired, and enjoy!

Chapter 4: Lunch Crunch

Eating a healthy lunch when you are limited on time due to, work, school, or taking care of your kids can be a tumultuous task. Thankfully, we have compiled a list of eight quick and easy recipes to accompany the ten day meal plan laid out in chapter 2! Many find it advantageous, especially if you work throughout the week, to prepare you meals ahead of time. Thankfully, these lunch recipes are also easy to pack and take on the go!

1. Off The Cobb Salad

- Net carbs: 3 grams
- Protein: 43 grams
- Fat: 48 grams
- Takes 10 minutes to prepare and serves 1.

What you will need:

- Spinach (1 cup)
- Egg (1, hard-boiled)
- Bacon (2 strips)
- Chicken breast (2 ounces)
- Campari tomato (one half of tomato)
- Avocado (one fourth, sliced)
- White vinegar (half of a teaspoon)
- Olive oil (1 tablespoon)

What to do:

1. Cook chicken and bacon completely and cut or slice into small pieces.
2. Chop remaining ingredients into bite size pieces.
3. Place all ingredients, including chicken and bacon, in a bowl, toss ingredients in oil and vinegar.
4. Enjoy!

2. Avocado and Sardines

- Net Carbs: 5 grams
- Protein: 27 grams
- Fat: 52 grams
- Takes 10 minutes to prepare and serves 1.

What you will need:

- Fresh lemon juice (1 tablespoon)
- Spring onion or chives (1 or small bunch)
- Mayonnaise (1 tablespoon)
- Sardines (1 tin, drained)
- Avocado (1 whole, seed removed)
- Turmeric powder (fourth of a teaspoon) or freshly ground turmeric root (1 teaspoon)
- Salt (fourth of a teaspoon)

What to do:

1. Begin by cutting the avocado in half and removing its seed.
2. Scoop out about half the avocado and set aside (shown below).
3. In small bowl, mash drained sardines with fork.
4. Add onion (or chives), turmeric powder, and mayonnaise. Mix well.
5. Add removed avocado to sardine mixture.
6. Add lemon juice and salt.
7. Scoop the mixture into avocado halves.
8. Dig in!

3. Chicken Salad A La Pesto

- This recipe requires 5minutes of preparation, 10 minutes of cooking time and serves 4
- Net Carbs: 3 grams
- Protein: 27 grams
- Fat: 27 grams

What you will need:

- Garlic pesto (2 tablespoons)
- Mayonnaise (fourth of a cup)
- Grape tomatoes (10, halved)
- Avocado (1, cubed)
- Bacon (6 slices, cooked crisp and crumbled)
- Chicken (1 pound, cooked and cubed)
- Romaine lettuce (optional)

What to do:

1. Combine all ingredients in a large mixing bowl.
2. Toss gently to spread mayonnaise and pesto evenly throughout.
3. If desired, wrap in romaine lettuce for a low-carb BLT chicken wrap.
4. Bon apatite!

4. Bacon and Roasted Brussel Sprouts

- This recipe requires 5 minutes of preparation, 30 minutes of cooking time and serves 4
- Net Carbs: 4 grams
- Protein: 15 grams
- Fat: 21 grams

What you will need:

- Bacon (8 strips)
- Olive oil (2 tablespoons)
- Brussel sprouts (1 pound, halved)
- Salt and pepper

What to do:

1. Preheat oven to 375 degrees Fahrenheit.
2. Gently mix Brussel sprouts with olive oil, salt, and pepper.
3. Spread Brussel sprouts evenly onto a greased baking sheet.
4. Bake in oven for 30 minutes. Shake the pan about halfway through to mix the Brussel sprout halves up a bit.
5. While Brussel sprouts are in the oven, fry bacon slices on stovetop.
6. When bacon is fully cooked, let cool and chop it into bite size pieces.
7. Combine bacon and Brussel sprouts in a bowl and you're finished!

8. Feast!!

5. Grilled Halloumi Salad

- Net Carbs: 7 grams
- Protein: 21 grams
- Fat: 47 grams
- Takes 15 minutes to prepare and serves 1.

What you will need:

- Chopped walnuts (half of an ounce)
- Baby arugula (1 handful)
- Grape tomatoes (5)
- Cucumber (1)
- Halloumi cheese (3 ounces)
- Olive oil (1 teaspoon)
- Balsamic vinegar (half of a teaspoon)
- A pinch of salt

What to do:

1. Slice halloumi cheese into slices 1/3 of an in thick.
2. Grill cheese for 3 to 5 minutes, until you see grill lines, on each side.
3. Wash and cut veggies into bite size pieces, place in salad bowl.
4. Add rinsed baby arugula and walnuts to veggies.
5. Toss in olive oil, balsamic vinegar, and salt.
6. Place grilled halloumi on top of veggies and your lunch is ready!
7. Eat those greens and get back to work!

6. Bacon Broccoli Salad

- This recipe requires 15 minutes of preparation, 6 minutes of cooking time and serves 5.
- Net Carbs: 5 grams
- Protein: 10 grams
- Fat: 31 grams

What you will need:

- Sesame oil (half of a teaspoon)
- Erythritol (1 and a half tablespoons) or stevia to taste
- White vinegar (1 tablespoon)
- Mayonnaise (half of a cup)
- Green onion (three fourths of an ounce)
- Bacon (fourth of a pound)
- Broccoli (1 pound, heads and stalks cut and trimmed)

What to do:

1. Cook bacon and crumble into bits.
2. Cut broccoli into bite sized pieces.
3. Slice scallions.
4. Mix mayonnaise, vinegar, erythritol (or stevia), and sesame oil, to make the dressing.
5. Place broccoli and bacon bits in a bowl and toss with dressing.
6. Viola!

7. Tuna Avocado Tartare

- Net Carbs: 4 grams
- Protein: 56 grams
- Fat: 24 grams
- Takes 15 minutes to prepare and serves 2.

What you will need:

- Sesame seed oil (2 tablespoons)
- Sesame seeds (1 teaspoon)
- Cucumbers (2)
- Lime (half of a whole lime)
- Mayonnaise (1 tablespoon)
- Sriracha (1 tablespoon)
- Olive oil (2 tablespoons)
- Jalapeno (one half of whole jalapeno)
- Scallion (3 stalks)
- Avocado (1)
- Tuna steak (1 pound)
- Soy sauce (1 tablespoon)

What to do:

1. Dice tuna and avocado into ¼ inch cubes, place in bowl.

2. Finely chop scallion and jalapeno, add to bowl.

3. Pour olive oil, sesame oil, siracha, soy sauce, mayonnaise, and lime into bowl.

4. Using hands, toss all ingredients to combine evenly. Using a utensil may breakdown avocado, which you want to remain chunky, so it is best to use your hands.

5. Top with sesame seeds and serve with a side of sliced cucumber.

6. There's certainly something fishy about this recipe, but it tastes great! Enjoy!

8. Warm Spinach and Shrimp

- This recipe requires 15 minutes of preparation, 6 minutes of cooking time and serves 5.
- Fat: 24 grams
- Protein: 36 grams
- Net Carbs: 3 grams
- Takes10 minutes to prepare, 5 minutes to cook, and serves 2.

What you will need:

- Spinach (2 handfuls)
- Parmesan (half a tablespoon)
- Heavy cream (1 tablespoon)
- Olive oil (1 tablespoon)
- Butter (2 tablespoons)
- Garlic (3 cloves)
- Onion (one fourth of whole onion)
- Large raw shrimp (about 20)
- Lemon (optional)

What to do:

1. Place peeled shrimp in cold water.
2. Chop onions and garlic into fine pieces.

3. Heat oil, in pan, over medium heat. Cook shrimp in oil until lightly pink (we do not want them fully cooked here). Remove shrimp from oil and set aside.
4. Place chopped onions and garlic into pan, cook until onions are translucent. Add a dash of salt.
5. Add butter, cream, and parmesan cheese. Stir until you have a smooth sauce.
6. Let sauce cook for about 2 minutes so it will thicken slightly.
7. Place shrimp back into pan and cook until done. This should take no longer than 2 or 3 minutes. Be careful not to overcook the shrimp, it will become dry and tough!
8. Remove shrimp and sauce from pan and replace with spinach. Cook spinach VERY briefly
9. Place warmed spinach onto a plate.
10. Pour shrimp and sauce over bed of spinach, squeeze some lemon on top, if you like, and you're ready to chow down!

Chapter 5: Thinner by Dinner

It's the end of the day and you are winding down from a hard day's work. Your body does not require a lot of energy while you sleep; therefore, dinner will typically consist of less fat and more protein.

1. Chicken Pad Thai

- Net Carbs: 7 grams
- Protein: 30 grams
- Fat: 12 grams
- Takes 15 minutes to prepare, 15 minutes to cook, and serves 4.

What you will need:

- Peanuts (1 ounce)
- Lime (1 whole)
- Soy sauce (2 tablespoons)
- Egg (1 large)
- Zucchini (2 large)
- Chicken thighs (16 ounces, boneless and skinless)
- Garlic (2 cloves, minced)
- White onion (1,chopped)
- Olive oil (1 tablespoon)
- Chili flakes (optional)

What to do:

1. Over medium heat, cook olive oil and onion until translucent. Add the garlic and cook about three minutes (until fragrant).

2. Cook chicken in pan for 5 to 7 minutes on each side (until fully cooked). Remove chicken from heat and shred it using a couple of forks.
3. Cut ends off zucchini and cut into thin noodles. Set zucchini noodles aside.
4. Next, scramble the egg in the pan.
5. Once the egg is fully cooked, and the zucchini noodles and cook for about 2 minutes.
6. Add the previously shredded chicken to the pan.
7. Give it some zing with soy sauce, lime juice, peanuts, and chili flakes.
8. Time to eat!

2. Chipotle Style Fish Tacos

- Fat: 20 grams
- Protein: 24 grams
- Net Carbs: 7 grams
- Takes 5 minutes to prepare, 15 minutes to cook, and serves 4.

What you will need:

- Low carb tortillas (4)
- Haddock fillets (1 pound)
- Mayonnaise (2 tablespoons)
- Butter (2 tablespoons)
- Chipotle peppers in adobo sauce (4 ounces)
- Garlic (2 cloves, pressed)
- Jalapeño (1 fresh, chopped)
- Olive oil (2 tablespoons)
- Yellow onion (half of an onion, diced)

What to do:

1. Fry diced onion (until translucent) in olive oil in a high sided pan, over medium- high heat.
2. Reduce heat to medium, add jalapeno and garlic. Cook while stir for another two minutes.
3. Chop the chipotle peppers and add them, along with the adobo sauce, to the pan.
4. Add the butter, mayo, and fish fillets to the pan.

5. Cook the fish fully while breaking up the fillets and stirring the fish into other ingredients.
6. Warm tortillas for 2 minutes on each side.
7. Fill tortillas with fishy goodness and eat up!

3. Salmon with Avocado Lime Sauce

- Net Carbs: 5 grams
- Protein: 37 grams
- Fat: 27 grams
- Takes 20 minutes to prepare, 10 minutes to cook, and serves 2.

What you will need:

- Salmon (two 6 ounce fillets)
- Avocado (1 large)
- Lime (one half of a whole lime)
- Red onion (2 tablespoons, diced)
- Cauliflower (100 grams)

What to do:

1. Chop cauliflower in a blender or food processor then cook it in a lightly oiled pan, while covered, for 8 minutes. This will make the cauliflower rice-like.
2. Next, blend the avocado with squeezed lime juice in the blender or processor until smooth and creamy.
3. Heat some oil in a skillet and cook salmon (skin side down first) for 4 to 5 minute. Flip the fillets and cook for an additional 4 to 5 minutes.
4. Place salmon fillet on a bed of your cauliflower rice and top with some diced red onion.

4. Siracha Lime Steak

- Net Carbs: 5 grams
- Protein: 48 grams
- Fat: 32 grams
- Takes 5 minutes to prepare, 10 minutes to cook, and serves 2.

What you will need:

- Vinegar (1 teaspoon)
- Olive oil (2 tablespoons)
- Lime (1 whole)
- Sriracha (2 tablespoons)
- Flank steak (16 ounce)
- Salt and pepper

What to do:

1. Season steak, liberally, with salt and pepper. Place on baking sheet, lined with foil, and broil in oven for 5 minutes on each side (add another minute or two for a well done steak). Remove from oven, cover, and set aside.
2. Place sriracha in small bowl and squeeze lime into it. Whisk in salt, pepper, and vinegar.
3. Slowly pour in olive oil.
4. Slice steak into thin slices, lather on your sauce, and enjoy!
5. Feel free to pair this recipe with a side of greens such as asparagus or broccoli.

5. Low Carb Sesame Chicken

- Net Carbs: 4 grams
- Protein: 45 grams
- Fat: 36 grams
- Takes 15minutes to prepare, 15 minutes to cook, and serves 2.

What you will need:

- Broccoli (three fourths of a cup, cut bite size)
- Xanthan gum (fourth of a teaspoon)
- Sesame seeds (2 tablespoons)
- Garlic (1 clove)
- Ginger (1 cm cube)
- Vinegar (1 tablespoon)
- Brown sugar alternative (Sukrin Gold is a good one) (2 tablespoons)
- Soy sauce (2 tablespoons)
- Toasted sesame seed oil (2 tablespoons)
- Arrowroot powder or corn starch (1 tablespoon)
- Chicken thighs (1poundcut into bite sized pieces)
- Egg (1 large)
- Salt and pepper

- Chives (optional)

What to do:

1. First we will make the batter by combining the egg with a tablespoon of arrowroot powder (or cornstarch). Whisk well.
2. Place chicken pieces in batter. Be sure to coat all sides of chicken pieces with the batter.
3. Heat one tablespoon of sesame oil, in a large pan. Add chicken pieces to hot oil and fry. Be gentle when flipping the chicken, you want to keep the batter from falling off. It should take about 10 minutes for them to cook fully.
4. Next, make the sesame sauce. In a small bowl, combine soy sauce, brown sugar alternative, vinegar, ginger, garlic, sesame seeds, and the remaining tablespoon of toasted sesame seed oil. Whisk very well.
5. Once the chicken is fully cooked, add broccoli and the sesame sauce to pan and cook for an additional 5 minutes.
6. Spoon desired amount into a bowl, top it off with some chopped chives, and relish in some fine dining at home!

6. Pan 'O Sausage

- Net Carbs: 4 grams
- Protein: 30 grams
- Fat: 38 grams
- Takes 10 minutes to prepare, 25 minutes to cook, and serves 2.

What you will need:

- Basil (half a teaspoon)
- Oregano (half a teaspoon)
- White onion (1 tablespoon)
- Shredded mozzarella (fourth of a cup)
- Parmesan cheese (fourth of a cup)
- Vodka sauce (half a cup)
- Mushrooms (4 ounces)
- Sausage (3 links)
- Salt (fourth of a teaspoon)
- Red pepper (fourth of a teaspoon, ground)

What to do:

1. Preheat oven to 350 degrees Fahrenheit.
2. Heat an iron skillet over medium flame. When skillet is hot, cook sausage links until almost thoroughly cooked.
3. While sausage is cooking, slice mushrooms and onion.

4. When sausage is almost fully cooked, remove links from heat and place mushrooms and onions in skillet to brown.
5. Cut sausage into pieces about ½ inch thick and place pieces in pan.
6. Season skillet contents with oregano, basil, salt, and red pepper.
7. Add vodka sauce and parmesan cheese. Stir everything together.
8. Place skillet in oven for 15 minutes. Sprinkle mozzarella on top a couple minutes before removing dish from oven.
9. Once 15 minutes is up, remove skillet from the oven and let cool for a few minutes.
10. Dinner time!

7. Quarter Pounder Keto Burger

- Net Carbs: 4 grams
- Protein: 25 grams
- Fat: 34 grams
- Takes 10 minutes to prepare, 8 minutes to cook, and serves 2.

What you will need:

- Basil (half a teaspoon)
- Cayenne (fourth a teaspoon)
- Crushed red pepper (half a teaspoon)
- Salt (half a teaspoon)
- Lettuce (2 large leaves)
- Butter (2 tablespoons)
- Egg (1 large)
- Sriracha (1 tablespoon)
- Onion (fourth of whole onion)
- Plum tomato (half of whole tomato)
- Mayo (1 tablespoon)
- Pickled jalapenos (1 tablespoon, sliced)
- Bacon (1 strip)
- Ground beef (half a pound)
- Bacon (1 strip)

What to do:

1. Knead mean for about three minute.

2. Chop bacon, jalapeno, tomato, and onion into fine pieces. (shown below)
3. Knead in mayo, sriracha, egg, and chopped ingredients, and spices into meat.
4. Separate meat into four even pieces and flatten them (not thinly, just press on the tops to create a flat surface). Place a tablespoon of butter on top of two of the meat pieces. Take the pieces that do not have butter of them and set them on top of the buttered ones (basically creating a butter and meat sandwich). Seal the sides together, concealing the butter within.
5. Throw the patties on the grill (or in a pan) for about 5 minutes on each side. Caramelize some onions if you want too!
6. Prepare large leaves of lettuce by spreading some mayo onto them. Once patties are finished, place them on one half of the lettuce, add your desired burger toppings, and fold the other half over of the lettuce leaf over the patty.

Burger time!

BREAKFAST

Breakfast Recipes To Start Your Day Strong

Sconey Sconey Sunday – 6 SmartPoints Per Serving

This breakfast dish is best made on the weekend and enjoyed all week long. This breakfast should be filling in the moment due to the fluffiness of the scone and should keep you satisfied all morning because of the liberal use of peaches. If you are new to baking, or just a little bit afraid of your own oven, this is a great recipe to start with. There is no need to wait for any ingredients to rise and it builds the foundation for many other scone recipes. You can replace the peach with blueberries, banana, apple, etc. Try and experiment to find what you like most.

Ready in 25 Minutes

10 minutes to prep and 15 minutes to cook

Ingredients (serves 4):

2/3 cups of all purpose flour

½ teaspoon of baking powder

½ teaspoon of baking soda

1 teaspoon of powdered sugar

2 tablespoons of sugar

½ teaspoon of half and half

1 teaspoon of margarine

1/3 cup of vanilla yogurt (I highly recommend Stoneyfield for the best results)

1 teaspoon of salt

3 tablespoons of chopped peaches (if you are using canned peaches, make sure you drain the peaches and give the peaches some time to dry. I recommend not using canned as they tend to contain additional sugars that add unnecessary calories and distort the flavor of the peaches)

Non-stick cooking spray

Step 1:

Preheat the oven to 400 degrees F or 205 degrees C

Step 2:

Take a medium size mixing bowl and add the flour, sugar (not powdered), baking powder, baking soda, and salt. Mix the ingredients and add in the margarine while doing so. The margarine can be difficult to work with so you may want to heat it up in a microwave for 15 seconds, or alternatively cut the margarine into small pieces. Only move onto step 4 when you have a consistent base in the bowl – the margarine should be fully mixed in.

Step 3:

Add the yogurt and the peaches, mixing while you do so.

Step 4:

Take a large piece of wax paper and empty the contents of the bowl onto the paper. Knead the dough for 3-4 minutes. Many are unsure of how to knead the dough, so think about it as folding the dough over itself over and over.

Step 5:

Coat a large baking tray with non-stick spray and form the scones on the tray. The scones look best when shaped like triangles. The exact size of the scones is not as important as making sure the scones are of equal size. This recipe usually yields between 4 and 6 scones. Make sure the dough is firmly pressed against the baking tray. Bake for 12-15 minutes on the center oven rack.

Step 6:

Remove the scones from the oven and while still hot, paint the scones with milk. This should look like they are slightly moist from the milk. Use this moisture to spread the powdered sugar over the scones. You can serve these right away and they will last about one week at room temperature.

10 Minute Fried Toast – 3 SmartPoints Per Serving

Yes this recipe is truly just a variation of French Toast but I want to stress the importance of a hot breakfast and that it doesn't take too much time to prepare one. This dish can be enjoyed even on a weekday before work and with a little practice you can cut down on the prep time dramatically. This is a dish I commonly make for my daughter before school and it can be made almost as fast as some simple scrambled eggs.

Ready in 10 Minutes

5 minutes to prep and 5 minutes to cook

Ingredients (serves 2):

4 egg whites

6 slices of wheat bread (you'll have lots of options of bread but I suggest looking at the low calorie version. I have switched to 40-45 calorie bread per slice and haven't noticed a big difference. The slices are a little smaller but each piece is less than half the calories of traditional white bread)

¼ cup of 1% milk

2 tablespoons of sugar free maple syrup (this recipe changes to 5 SmartPoints per serving with regular syrup)

1 tablespoon of cinnamon

1 tablespoon of vanilla extract

Non-stick cooking spray

Step 1:

In a shallow mixing bowl, add the egg whites, milk, and vanilla extract. Whisk these ingredients together.

Step 2:

Coat a skillet with cooking spray and put it over low-medium heat. Dip both sides of your wheat bread into the mixing bowl from step 1 and add to the skillet. You should be able to cook roughly 2 pieces at a time.

Step 3:

While still hot, sprinkle cinnamon on each piece of toast. Serve with syrup and enjoy right away.

3 Minute Breakfast Mug – 2 SmartPoints Per Serving

Perhaps you thought 10 minutes was too long to dedicate to cooking a warm breakfast, well then this recipe is for you. This is a breakfast I used to make at the office as the ingredients can be stored easily in a refrigerator. You will absolutely need to use the liquid egg substitute as opposed to liquid eggs as the substitute will cook better in the microwave. If you have never used your microwave as a primary cooking tool, do not fear – this too was my first recipe cooked entirely in a microwave. When you get a look at the finished product you will be highly satisfied with the result – it tastes great too.

Ready in 3 Minutes

1 minute to prep and 2 minutes to cook

Ingredients (serves 1):

½ cup of liquid egg substitute

1 ounce of low-fat turkey breast (optional)

1 slice of American cheese

Non-stick cooking spray

Step 1:

Take a microwave-safe mug and coat it with the non-stick spray.

Step 2:

Pour the egg substitute into the mug and microwave on high for 1 minute.

Step 3:

Add in the cheese and optionally the turkey. If you're adding the turkey, you will want to make sure that it is in very fine pieces. Microwave for an additional minute.

Saturday Morning Enriching Oatmeal – 7 SmartPoints

This filling breakfast will have you thinking differently about oatmeal. We take a hearty essential oatmeal recipe and add a combination of zesty flavors that make the dish shine. This breakfast takes longer than the others to cook and is best enjoyed on a weekend, or when you have some extra time before starting your day. This recipe can easily be doubled or tripled to serve the entire family.

Ready in 30 Minutes

10 minutes to prep and 20 minutes to cook

Ingredients (serves 1):

½ cup raw oats

2 teaspoons of lemon juice

1/8 teaspoon of cinnamon

1/8 teaspoon of salt

1 low-calorie sweetener packet similar to Splenda

1 cup of unsweetened almond milk, or vanilla soy milk

1 cup of water

Step 1:

In a small pot, combine the oats, cinnamon, salt, almond milk, and water.

Step 2:

Heat the pot on high heat and bring the oatmeal to a near boil. Once bubbling reduce the heat to low. Cook for 10-15 minutes after the oatmeal has been put to low heat.

Step 3:

Stir occasionally and remove from burner when the oatmeal has thickened.

Step 4:

Before serving, add the sweetener packet to the serving bowl.

LUNCH RECIPES THAT WILL KEEP YOU SATISFIED ALL AFTERNOON

Home Joe's Mediterranean Hummus With Pita Bread – 4 Smart Points Per Serving

This recipe is based on a small love affair I have for the Trader Joe's Mediterranean Hummus. I have tweaked this recipe to get very much the same taste, but with all the added benefit of knowing exactly what ingredients are used. This hummus is packed full of healthy fats from the chick peas, fats that will leave you satisfied all afternoon. I love to bring a small container to work and pair it with either pita chips or pita bread and a side of fresh vegetables – carrots and peppers in particular. Be on the lookout for the nutritional information on the chips or pita bread of your choice – while the hummus is healthy, aim for a serving of less than 200 calories for whatever you choose to dip in the hummus and add 2 smart points to the meal. Feel free to use as many veggies as you want for dipping though, think about these as 0 points.

Ready in 30 Minutes

30 minutes to prepare.

Ingredients (serves 8):

A food processor that can hold 3 cups

1 large garlic glove

2 tablespoons of tahini

½ lemon

6 tablespoons of extra virgin olive oil (the taste is important here, so use extra virgin instead of "pure")

¼ teaspoon of cumin

1 teaspoon of crushed red pepper

½ cup of boiling water

Step 0:

This recipe is dependent on your food processor. You won't need to prepare any ingredients, but make sure that your processor is up to the task. I have had this recipe come out just a tad too lumpy in the past because of the food processor, so blending time may vary slightly to get the consistency that you want.

Step 1:

Put the garlic clove and the processor and pulse 3 to 4 times. Add the rest of the ingredients except for the water.

Step 2:

Run the processor for 3-5 minutes, periodically switching from pulse to long sustained processing.

Step 3:

Pour in the hot water (does not need to be exactly boiling) and run the processor for an additional 30 seconds to a minute. Check the consistency of the hummus and run the processor for additional time if needed. You may need to add more than ½ a cup of water depending in the consistency of the beans and how powerful your food processor is.

Step 4:

With the desired consistency, pour the hummus in to a container and store in the fridge for several hours. Serving right away will not yield the best flavor as the ingredients are still settling.

Step 5 (Optional):

If serving for a party or if you simply want slightly more indulgent hummus, add a drizzle of olive oil to the hummus before serving.

5 Minute Turkey Wrap – 8 SmartPoints Per Serving

I ate these wraps nearly three times a week for half a year – they were just that delicious. They're easy to make and great to bring as a bagged lunch.

Ready in 5 Minutes

5 minutes to prep and 0 minutes to cook

Ingredients (serves 1)

3 ounces of low-sodium turkey breast (I encourage you to use your local deli counter versus the prepackaged meats – the deli counter meats will often have less sodium so even if you aren't purchasing 'low-sodium' turkey, it is probably still worth it to buy from the deli counter)

1 ounce of lettuce or spinach

¼ of one whole tomato

1 tablespoon of low-fat ranch dressing

1 ounce of low-fat mozzarella cheese (you can use other cheeses, but for the calorie to size ratio, I find mozzarella to be the best investment)

1 wrap or flatbread that is between 100-150 calories per wrap/flatbread (your supermarket will have several options for you but I suggest the Flatout Wraps. These wraps are fluffy and delicious are only 90 calories. For wraps above 150 calories, add another SmartPoint to the recipe)

Step 1:

Take out your wrap or flatbread and heat it in the microwave for 15-20 seconds – this will fluff up your wrap and make it more malleable to shape.

Step 2:

Spread your low-fat ranch dressing over the wrap. Fill the wrap with your turkey, lettuce or spinach, tomatoes, and cheese.

Step 3:

Roll up your wrap and store for lunch or eat right away.

Slow Cooker Southern Style Chicken Soup -4 SmartPoints Per Serving

It's an all day affair that that will last you all week and then some. This hearty soup is great in the winter and full of exotic blends of flavors that will have you wondering why you don't eat soup more often. Since this recipe produces a fairly large batch, it's worth noting that this soup freezes extremely well. If you decide to freeze individual servings, simply let the soup thaw at room temperature before you reheat in the microwave – this is the best way to preserve the flavor.

Ready in 7 Hours

10 minutes to prep and 6-8 hours to cook

Ingredients (serves 10)

2 large chicken breasts cut into inch size cubes

1 clove of finely minced garlic

1 cup of corn (canned is what I use)

½ diced large white onion

½ cup of finely chopped chilantro

1 teaspoon of cumin

1 tablespoon of chili powder

15 ounces of washed and drained kidney beans (canned is what I use)

15 ounces of washed and drained black beans (canned is what I use)

1 teaspoon of lime juice

2 whole bell peppers cut into long strips

1 15 ounce can of diced tomatoes

Pepper to taste

Salt to taste

Step 1:

Prepare all of your ingredients and pour them into your slow cooker. Put the slow cookers on low heat and let cook for 6-8 hours. To make sure that the soup is done, reach for a piece of chicken and slice to find the color in the center. Note that it is very difficult to overcook this recipe – even 9 hours in the slow cooker will result in a fantastic soup.

Alternative: If you do not have a slow cooker, do not fret – a regular pot on low heat on your burner will do just fine. There are some limitations however in that you will need to be present the entire time the soup is cooking. It is also possible to overcook the soup if you are using a traditional pot (I first made this recipe using this method and it turned out great. It does require time and patience if you're using a pot, but it can be made over the weekend and enjoyed all week long).

Healthy Zone Calzone – 4 SmartPoints Per Serving

I love this recipe because it uses a neat trick – we substitute heavy dough for Pillsbury and get to cut down on the cooking time in the process. This dish is great by itself and works great as a lunch served at room temperature. If you decide to make the marinara sauce in the next chapter, try it as a dipping sauce for this delicious healthy calzone.

Ready in 40 Minutes

25 minutes to prep and 15 minutes to cook

Ingredients (serves 8):

1 can of reduced fat crescent rolls by Pillsbury (this is absolutely necessary to get the right amount of dough to calorie ratio)

¼ cup of reduce fat shredded cheese (mozzarella is my go to choice but feel free to use your favorite).

6 ounces of low-fat chicken breast

2 cups of baby spinach

6 tablespoons of low-fat whipped cream cheese (you can also use reduced fat but know that it changes the total SmartPoints per serving quite significantly).

1-2 tablespoons of vegetable oil

Step 1:

Take the chicken breast and cut it into cubes before cooking in a frying pan. Use the vegetable oil to cook the chicken and try to use the least amount of oil possible. This recipe is extremely lean and the vegetable oil is actually one of the more calorie expensive ingredients – any savings here do add up.

Step 2:

Preheat the oven to 375 degrees F or 190 degrees C.

Step 3:

Remove the Pillsbury rolls and arrange them on an ungreased baking tray. The container should contain 8 rolls but we are only making 4 calzones. Combine rolls to make the 4 calzones and make sure each roll is flat on the tray.

Step 4:

Spread over each roll the baby spinach, cream cheese, chicken, and your choice of shredded cheese. These rolls are fairly small for how stuffed these calzones will be (definitely a good thing), so you may need to kneed some of the ingredients into the dough itself – this works particularly well with the cream cheese and shredded cheese.

Step 5:

Form each of the individual 4 calzones, fold the dough over the ingredients and 'close' the calzone. This step can be a little tricky if the dough is not at room temperature. The final shape should look a little bit like a crescent moon

Step 6:

Bake for 10-15 minutes in the middle rack of the oven. You will know when the calzones are ready as the dough will begin to flake and turn brown.

8 Minute Tuna – 3 SmartPoints Per Serving

I still prepare this Tuna Salad at least twice a month. It's quick and easy and great to bring to work. If you feel like you're missing out on the pure indulgence of 'fatty' flavors then this salad will hit the spot. Even though we are using low-fat mayonnaise, it still hits all the right notes and you'd be hard pressed to tell the difference between this and a much more calorie dense mayonnaise base. One of the greatest aspects of this recipe, and why it's only 3 SmartPoints per serving, is the use of lettuce as the base for wraps.

We use lettuce for a couple of reasons: one, the neutral flavor of the lettuce brings out the creaminess of the salad without distorting the taste and two, the crispness of the lettuce is essential for the proper texture. I came up with the idea for using lettuce as a base after eating Korean barbeque. Try it and you'll see how it really does bring out the flavor.

Ready in 8 Minutes

8 minutes to prep and 0 minutes to cook

Ingredients (serves 4):

12 ounces of albacore white tuna in water (essential as this tuna has the meatiest texture and taste)

3 tablespoons of low-fat mayonnaise

3 stalks o chopped celery (if any part of the stalk is not hard, then do not use that section. You want the celery to be firm as to add a crunchiness to the salad).

1 teaspoon of Dijon mustard

½ teaspoon of black pepper

½ teaspoon of table-salt (do not use sea-salt as the harsher grain does not spread as evenly throughout the salad)

½ head of lettuce cut into large pieces (these will serve as the wraps for eating the tuna so keep that in mind as you cut the lettuce)

Step 1:

Drain the tuna and add to a large mixing bowl. Add the celery, pepper, salt, mustard, and mayonnaise. Stir well, breaking up the large pieces of tuna that might be sticking together from the can.

Step 2:

For best results, leave the salad in the fridge for 20 minutes to let thicken. Serve with the large pieces of lettuce.

Week-Long Rice With Chicken – 4 SmartPoints Per Serving

One of the essentials of preparing a good lunch is not having to worry about side dishes. This dish comes with everything you need – protein to keep you full, carbohydrates to give you afternoon energy, and veggies for your general nutrition and to flavor the dish. This rice dish can be stored away for work and can be enjoyed at room temperature or even cold – it will still taste delicious!

Ready in 30 Minutes

15 minutes to prep and 15 minutes to cook

Ingredients (serves 6):

2 large lean, boneless chicken breasts

2 large eggs

2 cups uncooked brown rice

½ cup of pea

½ cup of chopped carrots

2 finely chopped cloves of garlic

2 tablespoons of soy sauce (1 tablespoon if using low-sodium soy sauce – better results are gotten with regular soy)

4 tablespoons of water

Non-stick cooking spray or if unavailable, 1 tablespoon of vegetable oil

Step 1:

Take the chicken breast and cut the chicken into long strips. The important part of cutting the chicken is that each strip has roughly the same thickness. Do not worry about how thick or thin your chicken is – just make sure it is fairy uniform.

Step 2:

Cook the brown rice on your stovetop. Use 5 cups of water for the 2 cups of brown rice. This is more water than is typically used and you will need to cook the rice for slightly longer. The rice will fluff up much more with that extra cup of water. Move onto step 3 only after the rice is done.

Step 3:

In a large skillet, scramble the two large eggs and set aside.

Step 4:

Coat the same skillet again with non-stick cooking spray. Each skillet is a little bit difference and if you know that non-stick spray is not going to be able to grease the entire pan, use 1 tablespoon of vegetable oil, as we do not want the chicken to stick to the pan. Add the sliced chicken and cook halfway before adding the carrots. As the chicken starts to look fully cooked, add the chopped garlic and peas.

Step 4:

Take the soy sauce and pour it into a small dish with the water. Mix and pour into the skillet. The water will evaporate and ensure that the soy sauce is not too overpowering. Move onto step 5 once the chicken is fully cooked and the water is mostly evaporated.

Step 5:

Add into the skillet the cooked rice and scrambled eggs. Mix well and remove from the burner once the eggs have warmed up. Serve right away.

Admiral David's Broccoli – 5 SmartPoints Per Serving

If the name seems familiar, or just a bit off, that's because it is indeed a variation of General Tso's Chicken. It's a standard American Chinese dish that incorporates crisp chicken, spice, and a tinge of orange flavoring. This recipe is derived from a dish a college roommate of mine used to make. If you guessed his name is David, then you would be correct. As with many of the other lunch dishes, this one is also great when served cold. This dish is a complete meal and doubles as a fantastic dinner that is quick to make.

Ready in 25 Minutes

15 minutes to prep and 10 minutes to cook

Ingredients (serves 4):

2 large chicken breasts

1 orange, cut and peeled

1 teaspoon of corn starch

4 teaspoon of vegetable oil

1 bag of precut broccoli florets (should equal roughly 2 cups)

1 tablespoon of minced ginger

¼ cup water (to mix with soy sauce)

3 tablespoons of soy sauce

¼ cup of orange juice

½ cup of chicken or vegetable broth

½ cup water (for help in cooking broccoli)

Step 1:

Take the chicken breasts and cut into long strips. Add the soy sauce to the ¼ cup of water and mix, set aside. During this step, make sure that your other ingredients are all set and ready to go. Once the pan heats up the cooking processes is very fast.

Step 2:

Add the vegetable oil to a large skillet warm over medium heat. Add the chicken strips and cook halfway – add the ginger and continue to cook the chicken until it is entirely done. Take the chicken and ginger out of the skillet and set aside.

Step 3:

Return to the skillet and add the broccoli. You should not need to add any additional oil but if when removing the chicken the pan was left dry, add an additional teaspoon. As the broccoli starts to lightly brown add the ½ cup of water and cover the skillet. Let the broccoli steam for 3 minutes. Check the broccoli to make sure that it is cooked through and not too raw.

Step 4:

Add the cooked chicken and ginger to the skillet. Add the soy sauce mixed with water, the orange juice, and the chicken broth. Mix these ingredients well and allow to cook for an additional 5 minutes. If the chicken or broccoli is beginning to be overcooked, change the heat to low or turn off the burner.

Step 5:

Add in the cornstarch and continue to mix. Once the cornstarch has been mixed in, add the orange peels to the top of the dish and cook for an additional minute or two. Serve right away.

DINNER RECIPES FOR THE HEALTHY BODY

Lightning Fast Curry Noodles – 3 SmartPoints Per Serving

This is a recipe I commonly refer to when I'm looking to make a quick dinner with just a bit of Asian flair. My favorite aspect to this recipe is that by using rice noodles you do not need to cook the noodles in a pot of boiling water. It can be made with just about any protein, including eggs or tofu. This particular version is vegetarian free, but adding cooked chicken or beef works just as well. This is my own recipe is supposed to mimic Singapore Noodles, a dish commonly found at Chinese restaurants throughout the country.

Ready In 20 Minutes:

10 minutes to prepare and 10 minutes to cook

Ingredients (serves 4)

3 large eggs

2 tablespoons whole milk (or half and half)

3 teaspoons of curry powder

2 tablespoons of vegetable oil

2 whole white mushrooms

1 bell pepper

1 package of Rice Noodles (you will want to go for medium thickness in the noodle – the particular brand does not matter)

2 tablespoons of soy sauce (low sodium soy sauce will *taste* more salty than regular soy sauce. If using low sodium soy then only use 1 tablespoon)

Step 1:

Take a large bowl or pot and fill it with warm water. The water does not need to approach boiling, and running hot water from your tap will suffice. Once the bowl is full, put the package of rice noodles into the water. You want to check back in a few minutes to make sure that every noodle is submerged in the water.

Step 2:

Slice the mushrooms and bell peppers into small slices. This dish will look a lot like a noodle stir fry, so cut the peppers in long strips and the mushrooms into thin slices.

Step 3:

While the noodles are soaking, use a small frying pan and with the milk and 3 eggs, make scrambled eggs. Once the eggs are made put them aside on a separate plate and cut the scrambled eggs into small pieces.

Step 4:

As the eggs are cooking, take a pan suitable for stir fry and add the vegetable oil. If you do not have a suitable stir fry pan, you can also use a standard pot for boiling pasta. Bring the heat to medium high and once the oil is hot add the mushrooms. As the mushrooms start to cook, add the peppers.

Step 5:

Strain the rice and noodles and add them to the pan with the mushrooms and the bell peppers. Note that the noodles should still appear to be a little bit brittle, do not worry as they will continue to cook in the pan.

Step 6:

As the noodles are cooking in the pan, add the soy sauce and mix thoroughly. Once the sauce is mixed, add the curry powder and stir thoroughly. The noodles should start to take on a dark yellowish color and at this point they should be thoroughly cooked through.

Step 7:

Add the cooked eggs to the pan, and then serve immediately. If the scrambled eggs are slightly cold, they will be warmed up through the cooked noodles.

Step 8:

Serve immediately and enjoy! This meal also works great for lunch. If you are unable to reheat the noodles while at work, they taste great just at room temperature.

Simple Season Chicken– 3 SmartPoints Per Serving

This recipe is a great healthy way to make seasoned chicken cutlets. These cutlets have just the right amount of seasoning and come packed with all the healthy protein of lean chicken breast. This recipe can altered slightly to make a lean type of chicken parmesan. See the altered steps 4 and 5 if you wish to go this route, otherwise this recipe is great with a side of spinach or any other side vegetable.

Ready In 35 Minutes

10 minutes to prepare and 25 minutes to cook

Ingredients (serves 4)

Chicken breast (use roughly 1 pound and cut into 4 large filets)

1/8 teaspoon paprika

¼ cup of parmesan cheese (grated finely)

½ teaspoon of garlic powder

1 teaspoon of parsley (optional)

black pepper to taste

3 tablespoons of dried breadcrumbs

Directions:

Step 1:

Preheat your oven to 400 degrees F or 205 degrees C

Step 2:

Take a small mixing bowl and add the breadcrumbs, grated parmesan, garlic powder, and paprika. Add a pinch of black pepper but know that you can add more while the chicken is cooking.

Step 3:

Take your sliced pieces of chicken breast and dip them into the bowl. Coat both sides of each piece of chicken. Since we are using a healthier version of traditional chicken parmesan, you might have some difficult having the mix stick to the chicken. It is best dip the chicken in the bowl right after you wash the chicken, using the moisture to get it to stick properly.

Step 4:

Prepare a nonstick baking tray and align the pieces of chicken towards the center of the baking tray.

Alternate for Chicken Parmesan: Using the Homemade Multi-Purpose Marina sauce (the next recipe in the book), lather the chicken liberally in 2-3 cups of sauce. You will need to use a deeper baking dish to cook the Chicken Parmesan. Once the sauce and chicken has been laid out, coat with shredded Parmesan Cheese and whole slices of mozzarella. To use an appropriate amount of cheese, only layer the cheese on top of the chicken filets. Note that this adds roughly 2 Smart Points to each serving.

Step 5:

Let the chicken bake in the oven for 25 minutes. Check at about 20 minutes as thinner pieces of chicken will cook more quickly. 25 minutes is around the upper limit for how long it will take to cook the chicken.

Alternate for Chicken Parmesan: Using the oven set to 400 degrees F, bake for 35-40 minutes.

Step 6: Remove the chicken form the baking tray and serve within 5-10 minutes.

Homemade Multi-Purpose Marinara – 3 Smart Points Per Serving

This is a great recipe to try out on the weekend and use all week long. Whether it's topping for Chicken Parmesan, dipping sauce for bread, or the foundation of a great pasta dish, this marinara sauce will leave you with plenty of options for how to enjoy it.

Ready in 30 Minutes

10 minutes to prepare and 20 minutes to cook

Ingredients (makes 1 quart)

2 large cloves of garlic

4 large tomatoes

1 28 ounce can of peeled tomatoes

3 tablespoons of olive oil (use extra virgin olive oil – the taste will make a huge difference)

1 ½ tablespoons of sugar

½ teaspoon of ground black pepper

1 teaspoon of salt

½ large white onion

Step 1:

Take your fresh tomatoes and dice them into small chunks. You can also optionally peel the skin from the tomatoes for a smoother sauce. During this step also chop your half onion and your garlic cloves.

Step 2:

In large sauce pan, heat the olive oil under a medium heat, add the diced onion. Wait until the onion is firmly sautéing before adding the garlic.

Step 3:

Add your chopped tomatoes and your can of tomatoes. Also stir in your black pepper and salt. Bring the heat up to medium high and wait for the sauce to boil. Stir frequently and let the sauce boil for 15 minutes.

Step 4:

Turn the heat down to low on the burner and let the sauce simmer for an additional 30 minutes.

Savory Grilled Salmon – 4 Smart Points Per Serving

If there's a common theme with this cookbook, it's the idea that healthy proteins are the foundation to a great diet. Even if you do not normally love salmon, or if you've never tried it, this recipe is certainly worth a shot. At 4 SmartPoints per serving, a side dish of potatoes and spinach will bring the total meal to a reasonable 6-7 SmartPoints, meanwhile the salmon will keep you full until morning.

Ready in 50 Minutes

30 minutes to prep and 20 minutes to cook

Ingredients (serves 4):

1 pound of skinless salmon fillet. You will want the thickness of the salmon to be about 1 inch.

¼ cup of soy sauce

Non-stick cooking spray

1 tablespoon of rice wine vinegar

¼ cup of dry sherry

1 tablespoon of brown sugar

1 teaspoon of garlic powder

1/8 teaspoon of ginger

Black pepper to taste

Step 1:

Preheat the oven to 375 degrees F or 190 degrees C. Make sure the grill rack is in the center of the oven.

Step 2:

Combine the sherry, soy sauce, brown sugar, vinegar, garlic powder, and ginger in a mixing bowl.

Step 3:

Dip the filets of salmon in the mixing bowl and place in the refrigerator for 20 minutes to marinade.

Step 4:

Place the remaining marinade in a small saucepan and heat on low. The marinade will begin to thicken as the salmon marinades in the refrigerator.

Step 5:

Spray the grill rack with non-stick spray and place the salmon filets on the rack. The cooking time for the salmon will differ greatly depending on thickness. As a guideline each side will need 4 to 8 minutes to cook through. The sign that the salmon is fully cooked is when it begins to flake.

Step 6:

Remove the salmon from the oven and place it on a large serving plate. Coat the salmon in the remaining marinade. Serve immediately.

Cheesy Baked Chicken – 5 SmartPoints Per Serving

I love this dish if for no other reason than it remind me that dieting does not need to omit cream and cheese. This chicken dish has all the flavor of a delicious casserole without any of the guilt. A simple side dish like a lightly tossed salad goes great, just be sure not to overdo it with the dressing.

Ready in 55 minutes:

10 minutes to prep and 45 minutes to cook

Ingredients (serves 8):

2 cups of cooked macaroni noodles

2 cups of 1% fat skin milk

2 cups of chopped boneless chicken breasts cut into cubes

8 ounces of low-fat shredded cheddar cheese

2 cups of undiluted cream of mushroom soup (I personally use Campbell's brand)

Step 1:

Preheat the oven to 350 degrees F or 175 degrees C.

Step 2:

Use a baking dish that is 2 inches deep, similar to a casserole dish, and place the cream of mushroom soup, the skim milk, cooked macaroni, shredded cheese, and uncooked chicken breasts into the baking tray. Mix thoroughly.

Step 3:

Place the baking tray in the center oven rack and bake for 35 minutes. At 35 minutes, take the baking tray out of the oven and remove a piece of chicken. Cut the chicken in half to see if it is cooked all the way through. Typically this recipe calls for 45 minutes, but if the chicken pieces are small enough the dish could be done in 35. Cook for an additional 10 minutes if needed.

Step 4:

45 minutes is the upper limit for cooking the casserole, but always make sure to slice the chicken and make sure that it is cooked all the way through. Small variables could mean cooking for an additional 5-10 minutes.

Step 5:

Let the dish cook for 10 minutes before serving.

Lean Mean Pork Chops – 3 SmartPoints Per Serving

In this recipe we are using our oven to bypass the unnecessary oil we'd get in by using a frying pan. This will lead to a more brazen pork that should be more tender. This dish takes longer than several of our other dinners and so use this time to experiment with side dishes. A vegetable melody goes great as the extra time gives you the opportunity to wash and cut your vegetables. You can also use the already heated oven for simple sliced baked potatoes – even the spices from the pork can be reused if you wish.

Ready in 70 Minutes

20 minutes to prep and 50 minutes to cook

Ingredients Needed (serves 4):

Non-stick cooking spray

1 large egg white

¼ teaspoon of ground ginger

1/8 teaspoon of garlic powder

2 tablespoon of pineapple juice

6 ounces of pork loin (try and get lean pork if available)

1 tablespoon of soy sauce

¼ teaspoon of paprika

1/3 cup dried breadcrumbs

¼ teaspoon of dried Italian seasoning

Step 1:

Preheat the oven to 350 degrees F or 175 degrees C

Step 2:

If you were able to purchase lean pork loin then you do not need to follow this step. If you were not able to purchase lean pork loin, trim away as much fat as you can. Do not worry about the taste – our seasoning will make up for the flavor.

Step 3:

In large mixing bowl, add the soy sauce, garlic powder, egg white, ginger, and pineapple juice. Mix well as the egg white is sometimes difficult to mix thoroughly.

Step 4:

Using a separate bowl, mix breadcrumbs, Italian seasoning, and the paprika.

Step 5:

Take the pork chops and dip them into the wet mixing bowl and then dip them into the dry mixing bowl. Coat the pork chops well but know that some ingredients will be left.

Step 6:

Lay the pork chops on the baking tray. Bake for 25-30 minutes on each side. Wait 3-5 minutes before serving.

Fast Cooking Scallops – 3 SmartPoints Per Serving

The hardest part of this recipe is the trip to the supermarket to purchase scallops. Do not fear as frozen scallops will work just fine, and if you are inexperienced cooking fish you also do not have to worry – this recipe is built upon the idea that perhaps this is your first time cooking fish in a pan. If you are unsure about whether to try this recipe, think about scallops as the 'meatier' shrimp. For a side dish, I recommend a baked potato and spinach or zucchini. The lemon goes great with subtle side dishes like these.

Ready in 20 Minutes

10 minutes to prep and 10 minutes to cook

Ingredients (serves 4):

1 pound of sea scallops, dried

2 tablespoons of all purpose flour

1 tablespoon of virgin olive oil

1 tablespoon of lemon juice

1 minced scallions

¼ teaspoon of salt

2 tablespoons of parsley

Pinch of sage (nice flavor, but not necessary if you don't already have this spice)

Step 1:

Take a mixing bowl and add the flour, scallions, and salt.

Step 2:

Take the scallops and dip them in the mixing bowl. Don't worry about how much of the mix ends up on the scallions – it should only be a small layer and does not necessary need to cover the scallops entirely.

Step 3:

Take a large skillet and heat the olive oil under medium heat. Toss the scallops one at a time into the pan. The scallops should could in about 4 minutes. Be careful not to overcook the scallops as they will become very though. You will know the scallops are done when they become impossible to see through the skin.

Step 4:

If the scallops were made in batches, add all of the scallops back into the pan, turning off the heat before you do so. Add the chopped parsley and lemon juice. Mix well and serve right away

CPSIA information can be obtained
at www.ICGtesting.com
Printed in the USA
LVHW081453171120
671610LV00012BB/492

9 789814 950909